# THE
# TWO CULTURES:
## AND
# A SECOND LOOK

AN EXPANDED VERSION OF THE
TWO CULTURES AND THE SCIENTIFIC
REVOLUTION

BY

## C. P. SNOW

CAMBRIDGE
AT THE UNIVERSITY PRESS
1964

PUBLISHED BY

THE SYNDICS OF THE CAMBRIDGE UNIVERSITY PRESS

Bentley House, 200 Euston Road, London, N.W.1
American Branch: 32 East 57th Street, New York 22, N.Y.
West African Office: P.O. Box 33, Ibadan, Nigeria

*Part I, First Printed* 1959
*Reprinted*   1959 (*three times*)
1960 (*three times*)
1961 (*twice*)
1962 (*twice*)

*Printed in Great Britain by Blackie & Son Ltd., Glasgow*

# CONTENTS

# PREFACE TO THE SECOND EDITION

Since the original lecture has been written about a good deal, I have thought it best to leave it as it was first printed, apart from the correction of two small inaccuracies.

In the second part, as I explain, I have looked at the lecture again in the light of various comments and the passage of four years.

*23 September 1963*                                              C.P.S.

# I. THE REDE LECTURE, 1959

## THE TWO CULTURES

IT is about three years since I made a sketch in print of a problem which had been on my mind for some time.[1] It was a problem I could not avoid just because of the circumstances of my life. The only credentials I had to ruminate on the subject at all came through those circumstances, through nothing more than a set of chances. Anyone with similar experience would have seen much the same things and I think made very much the same comments about them. It just happened to be an unusual experience. By training I was a scientist: by vocation I was a writer. That was all. It was a piece of luck, if you like, that arose through coming from a poor home.

But my personal history isn't the point now. All that I need say is that I came to Cambridge and did a bit of research here at a time of major scientific activity. I was privileged to have a ringside view of one of the most wonderful creative periods in all physics. And it happened through the flukes of war—including meeting W. L. Bragg in the buffet on Kettering station on a very cold morning in 1939, which had a determining influence on my practical life—that I was able, and indeed morally forced, to keep that ringside view ever since. So for thirty years I have had to be in touch with scientists not only out of curiosity, but as part of a working existence. During the same thirty years I was trying to shape the books I wanted to write, which in due course took me among writers.

There have been plenty of days when I have spent the working hours with scientists and then gone off at night with some literary colleagues. I mean that literally. I have had, of course, intimate friends among both scientists and writers. It was through living among these groups and much more, I think, through moving regularly from one to the other and back again that I got occupied with the problem of what, long before I put it on paper, I christened to myself as the 'two cultures'. For constantly I felt I was moving among two groups—comparable in intelligence, identical in race, not grossly different in social origin, earning about the same incomes, who had almost ceased to communicate at all, who in intellectual, moral and psychological climate had so little in common that instead of going from Burlington House or South Kensington to Chelsea, one might have crossed an ocean.

In fact, one had travelled much further than across an ocean—because after a few thousand Atlantic miles, one found Greenwich Village talking precisely the same language as Chelsea, and both having about as much communication with M.I.T. as though the scientists spoke nothing but Tibetan. For this is not just our problem; owing to some of our educational and social idiosyncrasies, it is slightly exaggerated here, owing to another English social peculiarity it is slightly minimised; by and large this is a problem of the entire West.

By this I intend something serious. I am not thinking of the pleasant story of how one of the more convivial Oxford greats dons—I have heard the story attributed to A. L. Smith—came over to Cambridge to dine. The date is perhaps the 1890's. I think it must have been at St John's, or possibly Trinity. Anyway, Smith was sitting at the right hand of the President—or Vice-Master—and he was a man who liked to include all round him in the conversation, although he was not immediately encouraged by the expressions of his neighbours. He addressed some cheerful Oxonian chit-chat at the one opposite to him, and got a grunt. He then tried the man on his own right hand and got another grunt. Then, rather to his surprise, one looked at the other and said, 'Do you know what he's talking about?' 'I haven't the least idea.' At this, even Smith was getting out of his depth. But the President, acting as a social emollient, put him at his ease by saying, 'Oh, those are mathematicians! We never talk to *them*.'

No, I intend something serious. I believe the intellectual life of the whole of western society is increasingly being split into two polar groups. When I say the intellectual life, I mean to include also a large part of our practical life, because I should be the last person to suggest the two can at the deepest level be distinguished. I shall come back to the practical life a little later. Two polar groups: at one pole we have the literary intellectuals, who incidentally while no one was looking took to referring to themselves as 'intellectuals' as though there were no others. I remember G. H. Hardy once remarking to me in mild puzzlement, some time in the 1930's: 'Have you noticed how the word "intellectual" is used nowadays? There seems to be a new definition which certainly doesn't include Rutherford or Eddington or Dirac or Adrian or me. It does seem rather odd, don't y' know.'[2]

Literary intellectuals at one pole—at the other scientists, and as the most representative, the physical scientists. Between the two a gulf of mutual incomprehension—sometimes (particularly among the young) hostility and dislike, but most of all lack of understanding. They have a curious distorted image of each other. Their attitudes are so different that, even on the level of emotion, they can't find much common ground. Non-scientists tend to think of scientists as brash and boastful. They hear Mr T. S. Eliot, who just for these illustrations we can take as an archetypal figure, saying about his attempts to revive verse-drama that we can hope for very little, but that he would feel content if he and his co-workers could prepare the ground for a new Kyd or a new Greene. That is the tone, restricted and constrained, with which literary intellectuals are at home: it is the subdued voice of their culture. Then they hear a much louder voice, that of another archetypal figure, Rutherford, trumpeting: 'This is the heroic age of science! This is the Elizabethan age!' Many of us heard that, and a good many other statements beside which that was mild; and we weren't left in any doubt whom Rutherford was casting for the role of Shakespeare. What is hard for the literary intellectuals to understand, imaginatively or intellectually, is that he was absolutely right.

And compare 'this is the way the world ends, not with a bang but a whimper'—incidentally, one of the least likely scientific prophecies ever made—compare that with Rutherford's famous repartee, 'Lucky fellow, Rutherford, always on the crest of the wave.' 'Well, I made the wave, didn't I?'

The non-scientists have a rooted impression that the scientists are shallowly optimistic, unaware of man's condition. On the other hand, the scientists believe that the literary intellectuals are totally lacking in foresight, peculiarly unconcerned with their brother men, in a deep sense anti-intellectual, anxious to restrict both art and thought to the existential moment. And so on. Anyone with a mild talent for invective could produce plenty of this kind of subterranean back-chat. On each side there is some of it which is not entirely baseless. It is all destructive. Much of it rests on misinterpretations which are dangerous. I should like to deal with two of the most profound of these now, one on each side.

First, about the scientists' optimism. This is an accusation which has been made so often that it has become a platitude. It has been made by some of the acutest non-scientific minds of the day. But it depends upon a confusion between the individual experience and the social experience, between the individual condition of man and his social condition. Most of the scientists I have known well have felt—just as deeply as the non-scientists I have known well—that the individual condition of each of us is tragic. Each of us is alone: sometimes we escape from solitariness, through love or affection or perhaps creative moments, but those triumphs of life are pools of light we make for ourselves while the edge of the road is black: each of us dies alone. Some scientists I have known have had faith in revealed religion. Perhaps with them the sense of the tragic condition is not so strong. I don't know. With most people of deep feeling, however high-spirited and happy they are, sometimes most with those who are happiest and most high-spirited, it seems to be right in the fibres, part of the weight of life. That is as true of the scientists I have known best as of anyone at all.

But nearly all of them—and this is where the colour of hope genuinely comes in—would see no reason why, just because the individual condition is tragic, so must the social condition be. Each of us is solitary: each of us dies alone: all right, that's a fate against which we can't struggle—but there is plenty in our condition which is not fate, and against which we are less than human unless we do struggle.

Most of our fellow human beings, for instance, are

underfed and die before their time. In the crudest terms, *that* is the social condition. There is a moral trap which comes through the insight into man's loneliness: it tempts one to sit back, complacent in one's unique tragedy, and let the others go without a meal.

As a group, the scientists fall into that trap less than others. They are inclined to be impatient to see if something can be done: and inclined to think that it can be done, until it's proved otherwise. That is their real optimism, and it's an optimism that the rest of us badly need.

In reverse, the same spirit, tough and good and determined to fight it out at the side of their brother men, has made scientists regard the other culture's social attitudes as contemptible. That is too facile: some of them are, but they are a temporary phase and not to be taken as representative.

I remember being cross-examined by a scientist of distinction. 'Why do most writers take on social opinions which would have been thought distinctly uncivilised and démodé at the time of the Plantagenets? Wasn't that true of most of the famous twentieth-century writers? Yeats, Pound, Wyndham Lewis, nine out of ten of those who have dominated literary sensibility in our time—weren't they not only politically silly, but politically wicked? Didn't the influence of all they represent bring Auschwitz that much nearer?'

I thought at the time, and I still think, that the correct answer was not to defend the indefensible. It was no use saying that Yeats, according to friends whose judgment I trust, was a man of singular magnanimity of character, as well as a great poet. It was no use denying the facts, which are broadly true. The honest answer was that there is, in fact, a connection, which literary persons were culpably slow to see, between some kinds of early twentieth-century art and the most imbecile expressions of anti-social feeling.[3] That was one reason, among many, why some of us turned our backs on the art and tried to hack out a new or different way for ourselves.[4]

But though many of those writers dominated literary sensibility for a generation, that is no longer so, or at least to nothing like the same extent. Literature changes more slowly than science. It hasn't the same automatic corrective, and so its misguided periods are longer. But it is ill-considered of scientists to judge writers on the evidence of the period 1914–50.

Those are two of the misunderstandings between the two cultures. I should say, since I began to talk about them—the two cultures, that is—I have had some criticism. Most of my scientific acquaintances think that there is something in it, and so do most of the practising artists I know. But I have been argued with by non-scientists of strong down-to-earth interests. Their view is that it is an over-simplification, and that if one is going to talk in these terms there ought to be at least three cultures. They argue that, though they are not scientists themselves, they would share a good deal of the scientific feeling. They would have as little

8

use—perhaps, since they knew more about it, even less use—for the recent literary culture as the scientists themselves. J. H. Plumb, Alan Bullock and some of my American sociological friends have said that they vigorously refuse to be corralled in a cultural box with people they wouldn't be seen dead with, or to be regarded as helping to produce a climate which would not permit of social hope.

I respect those arguments. The number 2 is a very dangerous number: that is why the dialectic is a dangerous process. Attempts to divide anything into two ought to be regarded with much suspicion. I have thought a long time about going in for further refinements: but in the end I have decided against. I was searching for something a little more than a dashing metaphor, a good deal less than a cultural map: and for those purposes the two cultures is about right, and subtilising any more would bring more disadvantages than it's worth.

At one pole, the scientific culture really is a culture, not only in an intellectual but also in an anthropological sense. That is, its members need not, and of course often do not, always completely understand each other; biologists more often than not will have a pretty hazy idea of contemporary physics; but there are common attitudes, common standards and patterns of behaviour, common approaches and assumptions. This goes surprisingly wide and deep. It cuts across other mental patterns, such as those of religion or politics or class.

Statistically, I suppose slightly more scientists are in

religious terms unbelievers, compared with the rest of the intellectual world—though there are plenty who are religious, and that seems to be increasingly so among the young. Statistically also, slightly more scientists are on the Left in open politics—though again, plenty always have called themselves conservatives, and that also seems to be more common among the young. Compared with the rest of the intellectual world, considerably more scientists in this country and probably in the U.S. come from poor families.[5] Yet over a whole range of thought and behaviour, none of that matters very much. In their working, and in much of their emotional life, their attitudes are closer to other scientists than to non-scientists who in religion or politics or class have the same labels as themselves. If I were to risk a piece of shorthand, I should say that naturally they had the future in their bones.

They may or may not like it, but they have it. That was as true of the conservatives J. J. Thomson and Lindemann as of the radicals Einstein or Blackett: as true of the Christian A. H. Compton as of the materialist Bernal: of the aristocrats de Broglie or Russell as of the proletarian Faraday: of those born rich, like Thomas Merton or Victor Rothschild, as of Rutherford, who was the son of an odd-job handyman. Without thinking about it, they respond alike. That is what a culture means.

At the other pole, the spread of attitudes is wider. It is obvious that between the two, as one moves through intellectual society from the physicists to the

gressive',[7] they know what they mean, even though it isn't what one is accustomed to expect.

Remember, these are very intelligent men. Their culture is in many ways an exacting and admirable one. It doesn't contain much art, with the exception, an important exception, of music. Verbal exchange, insistent argument. Long-playing records. Colour-photography. The ear, to some extent the eye. Books, very little, though perhaps not many would go so far as one hero, who perhaps I should admit was further down the scientific ladder than the people I've been talking about—who, when asked what books he read, replied firmly and confidently: 'Books? I prefer to use my books as tools.' It was very hard not to let the mind wander—what sort of tool would a book make? Perhaps a hammer? A primitive digging instrument?

Of books, though, very little. And of the books which to most literary persons are bread and butter, novels, history, poetry, plays, almost nothing at all. It isn't that they're not interested in the psychological or moral or social life. In the social life, they certainly are, more than most of us. In the moral, they are by and large the soundest group of intellectuals we have; there is a moral component right in the grain of science itself, and almost all scientists form their own judgments of the moral life. In the psychological they have as much interest as most of us, though occasionally I fancy they come to it rather late. It isn't that they lack the interests. It is much more that the whole literature of the traditional culture doesn't seem to them relevant to those interests. They are, of course, dead wrong. As a result, their imaginative understanding is less than it could be. They are self-impoverished.

But what about the other side? They are impoverished too—perhaps more seriously, because they are vainer about it. They still like to pretend that the traditional culture is the whole of 'culture', as though the natural order didn't exist. As though the exploration of the natural order was of no interest either in its own value or its consequences. As though the scientific edifice of the physical world was not, in its intellectual depth, complexity and articulation, the most beautiful and wonderful collective work of the mind of man. Yet most non-scientists have no conception of that edifice at all. Even if they want to have it, they can't. It is rather as though, over an immense range of intellectual experience, a whole group was tone-deaf. Except that this tone-deafness doesn't come by nature, but by training, or rather the absence of training.

As with the tone-deaf, they don't know what they miss. They give a pitying chuckle at the news of scientists who have never read a major work of English literature. They dismiss them as ignorant specialists. Yet their own ignorance and their own specialisation is just as startling. A good many times I have been present at gatherings of people who, by the standards of the traditional culture, are thought highly educated and who have with considerable gusto been expressing their incredulity at the illiteracy of scientists. Once or twice I have been provoked and have asked the company how many of them could describe the Second Law of Thermodynamics. The response was cold: it was also negative. Yet I was asking something which is about the scientific equivalent of: *Have you read a work of Shakespeare's?*

I now believe that if I had asked an even simpler question—such as, What do you mean by mass, or acceleration, which is the scientific equivalent of saying, *Can you read?*—not more than one in ten of the highly educated would have felt that I was speaking the same language. So the great edifice of modern physics goes up, and the majority of the cleverest people in the western world have about as much insight into it as their neolithic ancestors would have had.

Just one more of those questions, that my non-scientific friends regard as being in the worst of taste. Cambridge is a university where scientists and non-scientists meet every night at dinner.[8] About two years ago, one of the most astonishing discoveries in the whole history of science was brought off. I don't mean the sputnik—that was admirable for quite different reasons, as a feat of organisation and a triumphant use of existing knowledge. No, I mean the discovery at Columbia by Yang and Lee. It is a piece of work of the greatest beauty and originality, but the result is so startling that one forgets how beautiful the thinking is. It makes us think again about some of the fundamentals of the physical world. Intuition, common sense—they are neatly stood on their heads. The result is usually known as the non-conservation of parity. If there were any serious communication between the two cultures, this experiment would have been talked about at every High Table in Cambridge. Was it? I wasn't here: but I should like to ask the question.

There seems then to be no place where the cultures meet. I am not going to waste time saying that this is a pity. It is much worse than that. Soon I shall come to some practical consequences. But at the heart of thought and creation we are letting some of our best chances go by default. The clashing point of two subjects, two disciplines, two cultures—of two galaxies, so far as that goes—ought to produce creative chances. In the history of mental activity that has been where some of the break-throughs came. The chances are there now. But they are there, as it were, in a vacuum, because those in the two cultures can't talk to each other. It is bizarre how very little of twentieth-century science has been assimilated into twentieth-century art. Now and then one used to find poets conscientiously using scientific expressions, and getting them wrong—there was a time when 'refraction' kept cropping up in verse in a mystifying fashion, and when 'polarised light' was used as though writers were under the illusion that it was a specially admirable kind of light.

Of course, that isn't the way that science could be any good to art. It has got to be assimilated along with, and as part and parcel of, the whole of our mental experience, and used as naturally as the rest.

I said earlier that this cultural divide is not just an

English phenomenon: it exists all over the western world. But it probably seems at its sharpest in England, for two reasons. One is our fanatical belief in educational specialisation, which is much more deeply ingrained in us than in any country in the world, west or east. The other is our tendency to let our social forms crystallise. This tendency appears to get stronger, not weaker, the more we iron out economic inequalities: and this is specially true in education. It means that once anything like a cultural divide gets established, all the social forces operate to make it not less rigid, but more so.

The two cultures were already dangerously separate sixty years ago; but a prime minister like Lord Salisbury could have his own laboratory at Hatfield, and Arthur Balfour had a somewhat more than amateur interest in natural science. John Anderson did some research in inorganic chemistry in Leipzig before passing first into the Civil Service, and incidentally took a spread of subjects which is now impossible.[9] None of that degree of interchange at the top of the Establishment is likely, or indeed thinkable, now.[10]

In fact, the separation between the scientists and non-scientists is much less bridgeable among the young than it was even thirty years ago. Thirty years ago the cultures had long ceased to speak to each other: but at least they managed a kind of frozen smile across the gulf. Now the politeness has gone, and they just make faces. It is not only that the young scientists now feel that they are part of a culture on the rise while the other is in retreat. It is also, to be brutal, that the young scientists know that with an indifferent degree they'll get a comfortable job, while their contemporaries and counterparts in English or History will be lucky to earn 60 per cent as much. No young scientist of any talent would feel that he isn't wanted or that his work is ridiculous, as did the hero of *Lucky Jim*, and in fact, some of the disgruntlement of Amis and his associates is the disgruntlement of the under-employed arts graduate.

There is only one way out of all this: it is, of course, by rethinking our education. In this country, for the two reasons I have given, that is more difficult than in any other. Nearly everyone will agree that our school education is too specialised. But nearly everyone feels that it is outside the will of man to alter it. Other countries are as dissatisfied with their education as we are, but are not so resigned.

The U.S. teach out of proportion more children up to eighteen than we do: they teach them far more widely, but nothing like so rigorously. They know that: they are hoping to take the problem in hand within ten years, though they may not have all that time to spare. The U.S.S.R. also teach out of proportion more children than we do: they also teach far more widely than we do (it is an absurd western myth that their school education is specialised) but much too rigorously.[11] They know that—and they are beating about to get it right. The Scandinavians, in particular the Swedes, who would make a more sensible job of it than any of us, are handicapped by their practical need to devote an inordinate amount of time to foreign languages. But they too are seized of the problem.

Are we? Have we crystallised so far that we are no longer flexible at all?

Talk to schoolmasters, and they say that our intense specialisation, like nothing else on earth, is dictated by the Oxford and Cambridge scholarship examinations. If that is so, one would have thought it not utterly impracticable to change the Oxford and Cambridge scholarship examinations. Yet one would underestimate the national capacity for the intricate defensive to believe that that was easy. All the lessons of our educational history suggest we are only capable of increasing specialisation, not decreasing it.

Somehow we have set ourselves the task of producing a tiny *élite*—far smaller proportionately than in any comparable country—educated in one academic skill. For a hundred and fifty years in Cambridge it was mathematics: then it was mathematics or classics: then natural science was allowed in. But still the choice had to be a single one.

It may well be that this process has gone too far to be reversible. I have given reasons why I think it is a disastrous process, for the purpose of a living culture. I am going on to give reasons why I think it is fatal, if we're to perform our practical tasks in the world. But I can think of only one example, in the whole of English educational history, where our pursuit of specialised mental exercises was resisted with success.

It was done here in Cambridge, fifty years ago, when the old order-of-merit in the Mathematical Tripos was abolished. For over a hundred years, the nature of the Tripos had been crystallising. The competition for the top places had got fiercer, and careers hung on them. In most colleges, certainly in my own, if one managed to come out as Senior or Second Wrangler, one was elected a Fellow out of hand. A whole apparatus of coaching had grown up. Men of the quality of Hardy, Littlewood, Russell, Eddington, Jeans, Keynes, went in for two or three years' training for an examination which was intensely competitive and intensely difficult. Most people in Cambridge were very proud of it, with a similar pride to that which almost anyone in England always has for our existing educational institutions, whatever they happen to be. If you study the fly-sheets of the time, you will find the passionate arguments for keeping the examination precisely as it was to all eternity: it was the only way to keep up standards, it was the only fair test of merit, indeed, the only seriously objective test in the world. The arguments, in fact, were almost exactly those which are used today with precisely the same passionate sincerity if anyone suggests that the scholarship examinations might conceivably not be immune from change.

In every respect but one, in fact, the old Mathematical Tripos seemed perfect. The one exception, however, appeared to some to be rather important. It was simply—so the young creative mathematicians, such as Hardy and Littlewood, kept saying—that the training had no intellectual merit at all. They went a little further, and said that the Tripos had killed serious mathematics in England stone dead for a hundred years. Well, even in academic controversy, that took some skirting round, and they got their way. But I have an impression that Cambridge was a good deal more flexible between 1850 and 1914 than it has been in our time. If we had had the old Mathematical Tripos firmly planted among us, should we have ever managed to abolish it?

## INTELLECTUALS AS NATURAL LUDDITES

The reasons for the existence of the two cultures are many, deep, and complex, some rooted in social histories, some in personal histories, and some in the inner dynamic of the different kinds of mental activity themselves. But I want to isolate one which is not so much a reason as a correlative, something which winds in and out of any of these discussions. It can be said simply, and it is this. If we forget the scientific culture, then the rest of western intellectuals have never tried, wanted, or been able to understand the industrial revolution, much less accept it. Intellectuals, in particular literary intellectuals, are natural Luddites.

That is specially true of this country, where the industrial revolution happened to us earlier than elsewhere, during a long spell of absentmindedness. Perhaps that helps explain our present degree of crystallisation. But, with a little qualification, it is also true, and surprisingly true, of the United States.

In both countries, and indeed all over the West, the first wave of the industrial revolution crept on, without anyone noticing what was happening. It was, of course—or at least it was destined to become, under our own eyes, and in our own time—by far the biggest transformation in society since the discovery of agriculture. In fact, those two revolutions, the agricultural and the industrial-scientific, are the only qualitative changes in social living that men have ever known. But the traditional culture didn't notice: or when it did notice, didn't like what it saw. Not that the traditional culture wasn't doing extremely well out of the revolution; the English educational institutions took their slice of the English nineteenth-century wealth, and perversely, it helped crystallise them in the forms we know.

Almost none of the talent, almost none of the imaginative energy, went back into the revolution which was producing the wealth. The traditional culture became more abstracted from it as it became more wealthy, trained its young men for administration, for the Indian Empire, for the purpose of perpetuating the culture itself, but never in any circumstances to equip them to understand the revolution or take part in it. Far-sighted men were beginning to see, before the middle of the nineteenth century, that in order to go on producing wealth, the country needed to train some of its bright minds in science, particularly in applied science. No one listened. The traditional culture didn't listen at all: and the pure scientists, such as there were, didn't listen very eagerly. You will find the story, which in spirit continues down to the present day, in Eric Ashby's *Technology and the Academics*.[12]

The academics had nothing to do with the industrial revolution; as Corrie, the old Master of Jesus, said about trains running into Cambridge on Sunday, 'It is equally displeasing to God and to myself'. So far as there was any thinking in nineteenth-century industry, it was left to cranks and clever workmen. American social historians have told me that much the same was true of the U.S. The industrial revolution, which began developing in New England fifty years or so later than ours,[13] apparently received very little educated talent, either then or later in the nineteenth century. It had to make do with the guidance handymen could give it—sometimes, of course, handymen like Henry Ford, with a dash of genius.

The curious thing was that in Germany, in the 1830's and 1840's, long before serious industrialisation had started there, it was possible to get a good university education in applied science, better than anything England or the U.S. could offer for a couple of generations. I don't begin to understand this: it doesn't make social sense: but it was so. With the result that Ludwig Mond, the son of a court purveyor, went to Heidelberg and learnt some sound applied chemistry. Siemens, a Prussian signals officer, at military academy and university went through what for their time were excellent courses in electrical engineering. Then they came to England, met no competition at all, brought in other educated Germans, and made fortunes exactly as though they were dealing with a rich, illiterate colonial territory. Similar fortunes were made by German technologists in the United States.

Almost everywhere, though, intellectual persons didn't comprehend what was happening. Certainly the writers didn't. Plenty of them shuddered away, as though the right course for a man of feeling was to contract out; some, like Ruskin and William Morris and Thoreau and Emerson and Lawrence, tried various kinds of fancies which were not in effect more than screams of horror. It is hard to think of a writer of high class who really stretched his imaginative sympathy, who could see at once the hideous back-streets, the smoking chimneys, the internal price—and also the prospects of life that were opening out for the poor, the intimations, up to now unknown except to the lucky, which were just coming within reach of the remaining 99.0 per cent of his brother men. Some of the nineteenth-century Russian novelists might have done; their natures were broad enough; but they were living in a pre-industrial society and didn't have the opportunity. The only writer of world class who seems to have had an understanding of the industrial revolution was Ibsen in his old age: and there wasn't much that old man didn't understand.

For, of course, one truth is straightforward. Industrialisation is the only hope of the poor. I use the word 'hope' in a crude and prosaic sense. I have not much use for the moral sensibility of anyone who is too refined to use it so. It is all very well for us, sitting pretty, to think that material standards of living don't matter all that much. It is all very well for one, as a personal choice, to reject industrialisation—do a modern Walden, if you like, and if you go without much food, see most of your children die in infancy, despise the comforts of literacy, accept twenty years off your own life, then I respect you for the strength of your aesthetic revulsion.[14] But I don't respect you in the slightest if, even passively, you try to impose the same choice on others who are not free to choose. In fact, we know what their choice would be. For, with singular unanimity, in any country where they have had the chance, the poor have walked off the land into the factories as fast as the factories could take them.

I remember talking to my grandfather when I was a child. He was a good specimen of a nineteenth-century artisan. He was highly intelligent, and he had a great deal of character. He had left school at the age of ten, and had educated himself intensely until he was an old man. He had all his class's passionate faith in education. Yet, he had never had the luck—or, as I now suspect, the worldly force and dexterity—to go very far. In fact, he never went further than maintenance foreman in a tramway depot. His life would seem to his grandchildren laborious and unrewarding almost beyond belief. But it didn't seem to him quite like that. He was much too sensible a man not to know that he hadn't been adequately used: he had too much pride not to feel a proper rancour: he was disappointed that he had not done more—and yet, compared with *his* grandfather, he felt he had done a lot. His grandfather must have been an agricultural labourer. I don't so much as know his Christian name. He was one of the 'dark people', as the old Russian liberals used to call them, completely lost in the great anonymous sludge of history. So far as my grandfather knew, he could not read or write. He was a man of ability, my grandfather thought; my grandfather was pretty unforgiving about what society had done, or not done, to his ancestors, and did not romanticise their state. It was no fun being an agricultural labourer in the mid to late eighteenth century, in the time that we, snobs that we are, think of only as the time of the Enlightenment and Jane Austen.

The industrial revolution looked very different according to whether one saw it from above or below. It looks very different today according to whether one sees it from Chelsea or from a village in Asia. To people like my grandfather, there was no question that the industrial revolution was less bad than what had gone before. The only question was, how to make it better.

In a more sophisticated sense, that is still the question. In the advanced countries, we have realised in a rough and ready way what the old industrial revolution brought with it. A great increase of population, because applied science went hand in hand with medical science and medical care. Enough to eat, for a similar reason. Everyone able to read and write, because an industrial society can't work without. Health, food, education; nothing but the industrial revolution could have spread them right down to the very poor. Those are primary gains—there are losses[15] too, of course, one of which is that organising a society for industry makes it easy to organise it for all-out war. But the gains remain. They are the base of our social hope.

And yet: do we understand how they have happened? Have we begun to comprehend even the old industrial revolution? Much less the new scientific revolution in which we stand? There never was anything more necessary to comprehend.

## THE SCIENTIFIC REVOLUTION

I have just mentioned a distinction between the industrial revolution and the scientific revolution. The distinction is not clear-edged, but it is a useful one, and I ought to try to define it now. By the industrial revolution, I mean the gradual use of machines, the employment of men and women in factories, the change in this country from a population mainly of agricultural labourers to a population mainly engaged in making things in factories and distributing them when they were made. That change, as I have said, crept on us unawares, untouched by academics, hated by Luddites, practical Luddites and intellectual ones. It is connected, so it seems to me, with many of the attitudes to science and aesthetics which have crystallised among us. One can date it roughly from the middle of the eighteenth century to the early twentieth. Out of it grew another change, closely related to the first, but far more deeply scientific, far quicker, and probably far more prodigious in its result. This change comes from the application of real science to industry, no longer hit and miss, no longer the ideas of odd 'inventors', but the real stuff.

Dating this second change is very largely a matter of taste. Some would prefer to go back to the first large-scale chemical or engineering industries, round abou sixty years ago. For myself, I should put it much further on, not earlier than thirty to forty years ago— and as a rough definition, I should take the time when atomic particles were first made industrial use of. I believe the industrial society of electronics, atomic energy, automation, is in cardinal respects different in kind from any that has gone before, and will change the world much more. It is this transformation that, in my view, is entitled to the name of 'scientific revolution'.

This is the material basis for our lives: or more exactly, the social plasma of which we are a part. And we know almost nothing about it. I remarked earlier that the highly educated members of the non-scientific culture couldn't cope with the simplest concepts of pure science: it is unexpected, but they would be even less happy with applied science. How many educated people know anything about productive industry, old-style or new? What is a machine-tool? I once asked a literary party; and they looked shifty. Unless one knows, industrial production is as mysterious as witch-doctoring. Or take buttons. Buttons aren't very complicated things: they are being made in millions every day: one has to be a reasonably ferocious Luddite not to think that that is, on the whole, an estimable activity. Yet I would bet that out of men getting firsts in arts subjects at Cambridge this year, not one in ten could give the loosest analysis of the human organisation which it needs.

In the United States, perhaps, there is a wider nodding acquaintance with industry, but, now I come to think of it, no American novelist of any class has ever been able to assume that his audience had it. He can assume, and only too often does, an acquaintance with a pseudo-feudal society, like the fag-end of the Old South—but not with industrial society. Certainly an English novelist couldn't.

Yet the personal relations in a productive organisation are of the greatest subtlety and interest. They are very deceptive. They look as though they ought to be the personal relations that one gets in any hierarchical structure with a chain of command, like a division in the army or a department in the Civil Service. In practice they are much more complex than that, and anyone used to the straight chain of command gets lost the instant he sets foot in an industrial organisation. No one in any country, incidentally, knows yet what these personal relations ought to be. That is a problem almost independent of large-scale politics, a problem springing straight out of the industrial life.

I think it is only fair to say that most pure scientists have themselves been devastatingly ignorant of productive industry, and many still are. It is permissible to lump pure and applied scientists into the same scientific culture, but the gaps are wide. Pure scientists and engineers often totally misunderstand each other. Their behaviour tends to be very different: engineers have to live their lives in an organised community, and however odd they are underneath they manage to present a disciplined face to the world. Not so pure scientists. In the same way pure scientists still, though less than twenty years ago, have statistically a higher proportion in politics left of centre than any other profession: not so engineers, who are conservative almost to a man. Not reactionary in the extreme literary sense, but just conservative. They are absorbed in making things, and the present social order is good enough for them.

Pure scientists have by and large been dim-witted about engineers and applied science. They couldn't get interested. They wouldn't recognise that many of the problems were as intellectually exacting as pure problems, and that many of the solutions were as satisfying and beautiful. Their instinct—perhaps sharpened in this country by the passion to find a new snobbism wherever possible, and to invent one if it doesn't exist —was to take it for granted that applied science was an occupation for second-rate minds. I say this more sharply because thirty years ago I took precisely that line myself. The climate of thought of young research workers in Cambridge then was not to our credit. We prided ourselves that the science we were doing could not, in any conceivable circumstances, have any practical use. The more firmly one could make that claim, the more superior one felt.

Rutherford himself had little feeling for engineering. He was amazed—he used to relate the story with incredulous admiration—that Kapitza had actually sent an engineering drawing to Metrovick, and that those magicians had duly studied the drawing, *made the machine*, and delivered it in Kapitza's laboratory! Rutherford was so impressed by Cockcroft's engineering skill that he secured for him a special capital grant for machinery—the grant was as much as six hundred pounds! In 1933, four years before his death, Rutherford said, firmly and explicitly, that he didn't believe the energy of the nucleus would ever be released—nine years later, at Chicago, the first pile began to run. That was the only major bloomer in scientific judgment Rutherford ever made. It is interesting that it should be at the point where pure science turned into applied.

No, pure scientists did not show much understanding or display much sense of social fact. The best that can be said for them is that, given the necessity, they found it fairly easy to learn. In the war, a great many scientists had to learn, for the good Johnsonian reason that sharpens one's wits, something about productive industry. It opened their eyes. In my own job, I had to try to get some insight into industry. It was one of the most valuable pieces of education in my life. But it started when I was thirty-five, and I ought to have had it much earlier.

That brings me back to education. Why aren't we coping with the scientific revolution? Why are other countries doing better? How are we going to meet our future, both our cultural and practical future? It should be obvious by now that I believe both lines of argument lead to the same end. If one begins by thinking only of the intellectual life, or only of the social life, one comes to a point where it becomes manifest that our education has gone wrong, and gone wrong in the same way.

I don't pretend that any country has got its education perfect. In some ways, as I said before, the Russians and Americans are both more actively dissatisfied with theirs than we are: that is, they are taking more drastic steps to change it. But that is because they are more sensitive to the world they are living in. For myself, I have no doubt that, though neither of them have got the answer right, they are a good deal nearer than we are. We do some things much better than either of them. In educational tactics, we are often more gifted than they are. In educational strategy, by their side we are only playing at it.

The differences between the three systems are revelatory. We teach, of course, a far smaller proportion of our children up to the age of eighteen: and we take a far smaller proportion even of those we do teach up to the level of a university degree. The old pattern of training a small *élite* has never been broken, though it has been slightly bent. Within that pattern, we have kept the national passion for specialisation: and we work our clever young up to the age of twenty-one far harder than the Americans, though no harder than the Russians. At eighteen, our science specialists know more science than their contemporaries anywhere, though they know less of anything else. At twenty-one, when they take their first degree they are probably still a year or so ahead.

34

The American strategy is different in kind. They take everyone, the entire population,[16] up to eighteen in high schools, and educate them very loosely and generally. Their problem is to inject some rigour—in particular some fundamental mathematics and science —into this loose education. A very large proportion of the eighteen-year-olds then go to college: and this college education is, like the school education, much more diffuse and less professional than ours.[17] At the end of four years, the young men and women are usually not so well-trained professionally as we are: though I think it is fair comment to say that a higher proportion of the best of them, having been run on a looser rein, retain their creative zest. Real severity enters with the Ph.D. At that level the Americans suddenly begin to work their students much harder than we do. It is worth remembering that they find enough talent to turn out nearly as many Ph.D.s in science and engineering each year as we contrive to get through our first degrees.

The Russian high school education is much less specialised than ours, much more arduous than the American. It is so arduous that for the non-academic it seems to have proved too tough, and they are trying other methods from fifteen to seventeen. The general method has been to put everyone through a kind of continental Lycée course, with a sizeable component, more than 40 per cent, of science and mathematics. Everyone has to do all subjects. At the university this general education ceases abruptly: and for the last three years of the five-year course the specialisation is more intensive even than ours. That is, at most English universities a young man can take an honours degree in mechanical engineering. In Russia he can take, and an enormous number do take, a corresponding degree in one bit of mechanical engineering, as it might be aerodynamics or machine-tool design or diesel engine production.

They won't listen to me, but I believe they have overdone this, just as I believe they have slightly overdone the number of engineers they are training. It is now much larger than the rest of the world put together—getting on for fifty per cent larger.[18] Pure scientists they are training only slightly more than the United States, though in physics and mathematics the balance is heavily in the Russian direction.

Our population is small by the side of either the U.S.A. or the U.S.S.R. Roughly, if we compare like with like, and put scientists and engineers together, we are training at a professional level per head of the population one Englishman to every one and a half Americans to every two and a half Russians.[19] Some-one is wrong.

With some qualifications, I believe the Russians have judged the situation sensibly. They have a deeper insight into the scientific revolution than we have, or than the Americans have. The gap between the cultures doesn't seem to be anything like so wide as with us. If one reads contemporary Soviet novels, for example, one finds that their novelists can assume in their audience—as we cannot—at least a rudimentary acquaintance with what industry is all about. Pure science doesn't often come in, and they don't appear much happier with it than literary intellectuals are here. But engineering does come in. An engineer in a Soviet novel is as acceptable, so it seems, as a psychiatrist in an American one. They are as ready to cope in art with the processes of production as Balzac was with the processes of craft manufacture. I don't want to overstress this, but it may be significant. It may also be significant that, in these novels, one is constantly coming up against a passionate belief in education. The people in them believe in education exactly as my grandfather did, and for the same mixture of idealistic and bread-and-butter reasons.

Anyway, the Russians have judged what kind and number of educated men and women[20] a country needs to come out top in the scientific revolution. I am going to oversimplify, but their estimate, and I believe it's pretty near right, is this. First of all, as many alpha plus scientists as the country can throw up. No country has many of them. Provided the schools and universities are there, it doesn't matter all that much what you teach them. They will look after themselves.[21] We probably have at least as many pro-rata as the Russians and Americans; that is the least of our worries. Second, a much larger stratum of alpha professionals—these are the people who are going to do the supporting research, the high class design and development. In quality, England compares well in this stratum with the U.S.A. or U.S.S.R.: this is what our education is specially geared to produce. In quantity, though, we are not discovering (again per head of the population) half as many as the Russians think necessary and are able to find. Third, another stratum, educated to about the level of Part I of the Natural Sciences or Mechanical Sciences Tripos, or perhaps slightly below that. Some of these will do the secondary technical jobs, but some will take major responsibility, particularly in the human jobs. The proper use of such men depends upon a different distribution of ability from the one that has grown up here. As the scientific revolution goes on, the call for these men will be something we haven't imagined, though the Russians have. They will be required in thousands upon thousands, and they will need all the human development that university education can give them.[22] It is here, perhaps, most of all that our insight has been fogged. Fourthly and last, politicians, administrators, an entire community, who know enough science to have a sense of what the scientists are talking about.

That, or something like that, is the specification for the scientific revolution.[23] I wish I were certain that in this country we were adaptable enough to meet it. In a moment I want to go on to an issue which will, in the world view, count more: but perhaps I can be forgiven for taking a sideways look at our own fate. It happens that of all the advanced countries, our position is by a long way the most precarious. That is the result of history and accident, and isn't to be laid to the blame of any Englishman now living. If our ancestors had invested talent in the industrial revolution instead of the Indian Empire, we might be more soundly based now. But they didn't.

We are left with a population twice as large as we can grow food for, so that we are always going to be *au fond* more anxious than France or Sweden:[24] and with very little in the way of natural resources—by the standard of the great world powers, with nothing. The only real assets we have, in fact, are our wits. Those have served us pretty well, in two ways. We have a good deal of cunning, native or acquired, in the arts of getting on among ourselves: that is a strength. And we have been inventive and creative, possibly out of proportion to our numbers. I don't believe much in national differences in cleverness, but compared with other countries we are certainly no stupider.

Given these two assets, and they are our only ones, it should have been for us to understand the scientific revolution first, to educate ourselves to the limit and give a lead. Well, we have done something. In some fields, like atomic energy, we have done better than anyone could have predicted. Within the pattern, the rigid and crystallised pattern of our education and of the two cultures, we have been trying moderately hard to adjust ourselves.

The bitterness is, it is nothing like enough. To say we have to educate ourselves or perish, is a little more melodramatic than the facts warrant. To say, we have to educate ourselves or watch a steep decline in our own lifetime, is about right. We can't do it, I am now convinced, without breaking the existing pattern. I know how difficult this is. It goes against the emotional grain of nearly all of us. In many ways, it goes against my own, standing uneasily with one foot in a dead or dying world and the other in a world that at all costs we must see born. I wish I could be certain that we shall have the courage of what our minds tell us.

More often than I like, I am saddened by a historical myth. Whether the myth is good history or not, doesn't matter; it is pressing enough for me. I can't help thinking of the Venetian Republic in their last half-century. Like us, they had once been fabulously lucky. They had become rich, as we did, by accident. They had acquired immense political skill, just as we have. A good many of them were tough-minded, realistic, patriotic men. They knew, just as clearly as we know, that the current of history had begun to flow against them. Many of them gave their minds to working out ways to keep going. It would have meant breaking the pattern into which they had crystallised. They were fond of the pattern, just as we are fond of ours. They never found the will to break it.

## THE RICH AND THE POOR

But that is our local problem, and it is for us to struggle with it. Sometimes, it is true, I have felt that the Venetian shadow falls over the entire West. I have felt that on the other side of the Mississippi. In more resilient moments, I comfort myself that Americans are much more like us between 1850 and 1914. Whatever they don't do, they do react. It's going to take them a long and violent pull to be as well prepared for the scientific revolution as the Russians are, but there are good chances that they will do it.

Nevertheless, that isn't the main issue of the scientific revolution. The main issue is that the people in the industrialised countries are getting richer, and those in the non-industrialised countries are at best standing still: so that the gap between the industrialised countries and the rest is widening every day. On the world scale this is the gap between the rich and the poor.

Among the rich are the U.S., the white Commonwealth countries, Great Britain, most of Europe, and the U.S.S.R. China is betwixt and between, not yet over the industrial hump, but probably getting there. The poor are all the rest. In the rich countries people are living longer, eating better, working less. In a poor country like India, the expectation of life is less than half what it is in England. There is some evidence that Indians and other Asians are eating less, in absolute quantities, than they were a generation ago. The statistics are not reliable, and informants in the F.A.O. have told me not to put much trust in them. But it is accepted that, in all non-industrialised countries, people are not eating better than at the subsistence level. And they are working as people have always had to work, from Neolithic times until our own. Life for the over-whelming majority of mankind has always been nasty, brutish and short. It is so in the poor countries still.

This disparity between the rich and the poor has been noticed. It has been noticed, most acutely and not un-naturally, by the poor. Just because they have noticed it, it won't last for long. Whatever else in the world we know survives to the year 2000, that won't. Once the trick of getting rich is known, as it now is, the world can't survive half rich and half poor. It's just not on.

The West has got to help in this transformation. The trouble is, the West with its divided culture finds it hard to grasp just how big, and above all just how fast, the transformation must be.

Earlier I said that few non-scientists really under-stand the scientific concept of acceleration. I meant that as a gibe. But in social terms, it is a little more than a gibe. During all human history until this century, the rate of social change has been very slow. So slow, that it would pass unnoticed in one person's lifetime. That is no longer so. The rate of change has increased so much that our imagination can't keep up. There is *bound* to be more social change, affecting more people, in the next decade than in any before. There is *bound* to be more change again, in the 1970's. In the poor countries, people have caught on to this simple concept. Men there are no longer prepared to wait for periods longer than one person's lifetime.

The comforting assurances, given *de haut en bas*, that maybe in a hundred or two hundred years things may be slightly better for them—they only madden. Pronouncements such as one still hears from old Asia or old Africa hands—Why, it will take those people five hundred years to get up to our standard!—they are both suicidal and technologically illiterate. Particularly when said, as they always seem to be said, by someone looking as though it wouldn't take Neanderthal Man five years to catch up with *him*.

The fact is, the rate of change has already been proved possible. Someone said, when the first atomic bomb went off, that the only important secret is now let out—the thing works. After that, any determined country could make the bomb, given a few years. In the same way, the only secret of the Russian and Chinese industrialisation is that they've brought it off. That is what Asians and Africans have noticed. It took the Russians about forty years, starting with something of an industrial base—Tsarist industry wasn't negligible—but interrupted by a civil war and then the greatest war of all. The Chinese started with much less of an industrial base, but haven't been interrupted, and it looks like taking them not much over half the time.

These transformations were made with inordinate effort and with great suffering. Much of the suffering was unnecessary: the horror is hard to look at straight, standing in the same decades. Yet they've proved that common men can show astonishing fortitude in chasing jam tomorrow. Jam today, and men aren't at their most exciting: jam tomorrow, and one often sees them at their noblest. The transformations have also proved something which only the scientific culture can take in its stride. Yet, when we don't take it in our stride, it makes us look silly.

It is simply that technology is rather easy. Or more exactly, technology is the branch of human experience that people can learn with predictable results. For a long time, the West misjudged this very badly. After all, a good many Englishmen have been skilled in mechanical crafts for half-a-dozen generations. Somehow we've made ourselves believe that the whole of technology was a more or less incommunicable art. It's true enough, we start with a certain advantage. Not so much because of tradition, I think, as because all our children play with mechanical toys. They are picking up pieces of applied science before they can read. That is an advantage we haven't made the most of. Just as the Americans have the advantage that nine out of ten adults can drive a car and are to some extent mechanics. In the last war, which was a war of small machines, that was a real military asset. Russia is catching up with the U.S. in major industry—but it will be a long time before Russia is as convenient a country as the U.S. in which to have one's car break down.[25]

The curious thing is, none of that seems to matter much. For the task of totally industrialising a major country, as in China today, it only takes will to train enough scientists and engineers and technicians. Will, and quite a small number of years. There is no evidence that any country or race is better than any other in scientific teachability: there is a good deal of evidence that all are much alike. Tradition and technical background seem to count for surprisingly little.

We've all seen this with our own eyes. I myself have found Sicilian girls taking the top places in the Honours Physics course—a very exacting course—at the University of Rome: they'd have been in something like purdah thirty years ago. And I remember John Cockcroft coming back from Moscow some time in the early 1930's. The news got round that he had been able to have a look, not only at laboratories, but at factories and the mechanics in them. What we expected to hear, I don't know: but there were certainly some who had pleasurable expectations of those stories precious to the hearts of western man, about moujiks prostrating themselves before a milling machine, or breaking a vertical borer with their bare hands. Someone asked Cockcroft what the skilled workmen were like. Well, he has never been a man to waste words. A fact is a fact is a fact. 'Oh,' he said, 'they're just about the same as the ones at Metrovick.' That was all. He was, as usual, right.

There is no getting away from it. It is technically possible to carry out the scientific revolution in India, Africa, South-east Asia, Latin America, the Middle East, within fifty years. There is no excuse for western man not to know this. And not to know that this is the one way out through the three menaces which stand in our way—H-bomb war, over-population, the gap between the rich and the poor. This is one of the situations where the worst crime is innocence.

Since the gap between the rich countries and the poor can be removed, it will be. If we are short-sighted, inept, incapable either of good-will or en-lightened self-interest, then it may be removed to the accompaniment of war and starvation: but removed it will be. The questions are, how, and by whom. To those questions, one can only give partial answers: but that may be enough to set us thinking. The scientific revolution on the world-scale needs, first and fore-most, capital: capital in all forms, including capital machinery. The poor countries, until they have got beyond a certain point on the industrial curve cannot accumulate that capital. That is why the gap between rich and poor is widening. The capital must come from outside.

There are only two possible sources. One is the West, which means mainly the U.S., the other is the U.S.S.R. Even the United States hasn't infinite re-sources of such capital. If they or Russia tried to do it alone, it would mean an effort greater than either had to make industrially in the war. If they both took part, it wouldn't mean that order of sacrifice—though in my view it's optimistic to think, as some wise men do, that it would mean no sacrifice at all. The scale of the operation requires that it would have to be a national one. Private industry, even the biggest private industry, can't touch it, and in no sense is it a fair business risk. It's a bit like asking Duponts or I.C.I. back in 1940 to finance the entire development of the atomic bomb.

The second requirement, after capital, as important as capital, is men. That is, trained scientists and engineers adaptable enough to devote themselves to a foreign country's industrialisation for at least ten years out of their lives. Here, unless and until the Americans and we educate ourselves both sensibly and imaginatively, the Russians have a clear edge. This is where their educational policy has already paid big dividends. They have such men to spare if they are needed. We just haven't, and the Americans aren't much better off. Imagine, for example, that the U.S. government and ours had agreed to help the Indians to carry out a major industrialisation, similar in scale to the Chinese. Imagine that the capital could be found. It would then require something like ten thousand to twenty thousand engineers from the U.S. and here to help get the thing going. At present, we couldn't find them.

These men, whom we don't yet possess, need to be trained not only in scientific but in human terms. They could not do their job if they did not shrug off every trace of paternalism. Plenty of Europeans, from St Francis Xavier to Schweitzer, have devoted their lives to Asians and Africans, nobly but paternally. These are not the Europeans whom Asians and Africans are going to welcome now. They want men who will muck in as colleagues, who will pass on what they know, do an honest technical job, and get out. Fortunately, this is an attitude which comes easily to scientists. They are freer than most people from racial feeling; their own culture is in its human relations a democratic one. In their own internal climate, the breeze of the equality of man hits you in the face, sometimes rather roughly, just as it does in Norway.

That is why scientists would do us good all over Asia and Africa. And they would do their part too in the third essential of the scientific revolution—which, in a country like India, would have to run in parallel with the capital investment and the initial foreign help. That is, an educational programme as complete as the Chinese, who appear in ten years to have transformed their universities and built so many new ones that they are now nearly independent of scientists and engineers from outside. Ten years. With scientific teachers from this country and the U.S., and what is also necessary, with teachers of English, other poor countries could do the same in twenty.

That is the size of the problem. An immense capital outlay, an immense investment in men, both scientists and linguists, most of whom the West does not yet possess. With rewards negligible in the short term, apart from doing the job: and in the long term most uncertain.

People will ask me, in fact in private they have already asked me—'This is all very fine and large. But you are supposed to be a realistic man. You are interested in the fine structure of politics; you have spent some time studying how men behave in the pursuit of their own ends. Can you possibly believe that men will behave as you say they ought to? Can you imagine a political technique, in parliamentary societies like the U.S. or our own, by which any such plan could become real? Do you really believe that there is one chance in ten that any of this will happen?'

That is fair comment. I can only reply that I don't know. On the one hand, it is a mistake, and it is a mistake, of course, which anyone who is called realistic is specially liable to fall into, to think that when we have said something about the egotisms, the weaknesses, the vanities, the power-seekings of men, that we have said everything. Yes, they are like that. They are the bricks with which we have got to build, and one can judge them through the extent of one's own selfishness. But they are sometimes capable of more, and any 'realism' which doesn't admit of that isn't serious.

On the other hand, I confess, and I should be less than honest if I didn't, that I can't see the political techniques through which the good human capabilities of the West can get into action. The best one can do, and it is a poor best, is to nag away. That is perhaps too easy

49

a palliative for one's disquiet. For, though I don't know how we can do what we need to do, or whether we shall do anything at all, I do know this: that, if we don't do it, the Communist countries will in time. They will do it at great cost to themselves and others, but they will do it. If that is how it turns out, we shall have failed, both practically and morally. At best, the West will have become an *enclave* in a different world—and this country will be the *enclave* of an *enclave*. Are we resigning ourselves to that? History is merciless to failure. In any case, if that happens, we shall not be writing the history.

Meanwhile, there are steps to be taken which aren't outside the powers of reflective people. Education isn't the total solution to this problem: but without education the West can't even begin to cope. All the arrows point the same way. Closing the gap between our cultures is a necessity in the most abstract intellectual sense, as well as in the most practical. When those two senses have grown apart, then no society is going to be able to think with wisdom. For the sake of the intellectual life, for the sake of this country's special danger, for the sake of the western society living precariously rich among the poor, for the sake of the poor who needn't be poor if there is intelligence in the world, it is obligatory for us and the Americans and the whole West to look at our education with fresh eyes. This is one of the cases where we and the Americans have the most to learn from each other. We have each a good deal to learn from the Russians, if we are not too proud. Incidentally, the Russians have a good deal to learn from us, too.

Isn't it time we began? The danger is, we have been brought up to think as though we had all the time in the world. We have very little time. So little that I dare not guess at it.

## II.   THE TWO CULTURES:
## A SECOND LOOK

### § I

IT is over four years since (in May 1959) I gave the
Rede Lecture at Cambridge. I chose a subject
which several of us had been discussing for some
time past. I hoped at most to act as a goad to action,
first in education and second—in my own mind the
latter part of the lecture was always the more pressing
—in sharpening the concern of rich and privileged
societies for those less lucky. I did not expect much.
Plenty of people were saying similar things. It seemed
to me to be a time when one should add one's voice.
I thought I might be listened to in some restricted
circles. Then the effect would soon die down: and
in due course, since I was deeply committed, I should
feel obliged to have another go.

For a while that appeared to be a reasonable prog-
nosis. According to precedent, the lecture was
published, as a paper-covered pamphlet,[26] the day
after it was delivered. It received some editorial
attention, but, in the first months, not many reviews.
There was not, and could not be, any advertising.
*Encounter* published long extracts, and these drew
some comment.[27] I had a number of interesting
private letters. That, I thought, was the end of it.

It did not turn out quite like that. By the end of the first year I began to feel uncomfortably like the sorcerer's apprentice. Articles, references, letters, blame, praise, were floating in—often from countries where I was otherwise unknown. The whole phenomenon, in fact, as I shall shortly explain, hadn't much connection with me. It was a curious, rather than a pleasurable, experience. The literature has gone on accumulating at an accelerating pace: I suppose I must, by the nature of things, have seen more of it than anyone else; but I have not seen anything like the whole. And it is frustrating to be told that some of the more valuable discussions have been taking place in languages not accessible to most Englishmen, such as Hungarian, Polish and Japanese.

As the flood of literature mounted, two deductions became self-evident. The first was that if a nerve had been touched almost simultaneously in different intellectual societies, in different parts of the world, the ideas which produced this response couldn't possibly be original. Original ideas don't carry at that speed. Very occasionally one thinks or hopes that one has said something new: and waits a little bleakly for years, in the hope that it will strike a spark of recognition somewhere. This was quite different. It was clear that many people had been thinking on this assembly of topics. The ideas were in the air. Anyone, anywhere, had only to choose a form of words. Then—click, the trigger was pressed. The words need not be the right words: but the time, which no-one could predict beforehand, had to be the right time. When that happened, the sorcerer's apprentice was left to look at the water rushing in.

It seems to be pure chance that others had not found themselves, some time earlier, in the same apprentice-like position. Jacob Bronowski had, at various times in the fifties,[28] dealt imaginatively with many aspects of these problems. Merle Kling in 1957 published an article[29]—unknown to me until much later—which closely anticipated the first half of my lecture. Professional educators such as A. D. C. Peterson had done much the same. In 1956[30] and 1957[31] I myself wrote two pieces which, though shorter than the Rede Lecture, contained much of its substance. Yet none of us got much response. Two years later the time was right; and any one of us could have produced a hubbub. It is a reminder of the mysterious operation of what, in the nineteenth century, was reverently referred to as the *Zeitgeist*.

The first deduction, then, is that these ideas were not at all original, but were waiting in the air. The second deduction is, I think, equally obvious. It is, that there must be something in them. I don't mean that they are necessarily right; I don't mean that they couldn't have been expressed in many different or better forms: but contained in them or hidden beneath them, there is something which people, all over the world, suspect is relevant to present actions. It would not have mattered whether these things were said by me or Bronowski or Kling, or A or B or C. A complex argument started, and will go on. This could not have happened adventitiously. It certainly could not have happened through any personal impact. On these issues our personalities mean nothing: but the issues themselves mean a good deal.

The sheer volume of comment has been formidable, some of it agreeing with me, some cross-bench, and some disagreeing. Many of the criticisms I respect. I have not replied to them piecemeal, since I have been following a rule which I have set myself in other controversies. It seems to me that engaging in immediate debate on each specific point closes one's own mind for good and all. Debating gives most of us much more psychological satisfaction than thinking does: but it deprives us of whatever chance there is of getting closer to the truth. It seems preferable to me to sit back and let what has been said sink in—I don't pretend this is altogether easy—and then, after a longish interval, with the advantage of what I have heard and of new knowledge, see what modifications I should make if I were going to give the lecture again. This is what I am doing now. I intend to continue the same practice in the future. If I think I have anything further to add, I shall leave it for some time.

During the arguments so far, there has been one unusual manifestation, which I shall mention just to get it out of the way. A few, a very few, of the

criticisms have been loaded with personal abuse to
an abnormal extent: to such an extent in one case, in
fact, that the persons responsible for its publication in
two different media[32] made separate approaches to
me, in order to obtain my consent. I had to assure
them that I did not propose to take legal action. All
this seemed to me distinctly odd. In any dispute
acrimonious words are likely to fly about, but it is
not common, at least in my experience, for them to
come anywhere near the limit of defamation.

However, the problem of behaviour in these circumstances is very easily solved. Let us imagine that
I am called, in print, a kleptomaniac necrophilist (I
have selected with some care two allegations which
have not, so far as I know, been made). I have exactly
two courses of action. The first, and the one which
in general I should choose to follow, is to do precisely
nothing. The second is, if the nuisance becomes
intolerable, to sue. There is one course of action
which no one can expect of a sane man: that is,
solemnly to argue the points, to produce certificates
from Saks and Harrods to say he has never, to the
best of their belief, stolen a single article, to obtain
testimonials signed by sixteen Fellows of the Royal
Society, the Head of the Civil Service, a Lord Justice
of Appeal and the Secretary of the M.C.C., testifying
that they have known him for half a lifetime, and
that even after a convivial evening they have not
once seen him lurking in the vicinity of a tomb.

Such a reply is not on. It puts one in the same

psychological compartment as one's traducer. That is a condition from which one has a right to be excused.

The argument, fortunately, will suffer no loss if we ignore criticisms of this particular spirit, and any associated with them: for such intellectual contributions as they contain have been made, with civility and seriousness, by others.

There will need to be some cleaning up in due course. Textbook examples of the effects of some psychological states are not always conveniently come by: but a good many exist in this section of the literature. Do certain kinds of animosity lead to an inability to perform the physical act of reading? The evidence suggests so. The original lecture was quite short. The text is very simple. Most people, more particularly when attacking with virulence, would take pains to get straightforward quotations right. Yet this has not happened. There are various examples which, like the whole episode, seem to me somewhat bizarre. I will just select the crudest. One of my outrages in the Rede Lecture has been said to be the use of a phrase—'We die alone'. This phrase has been quoted and brandished, not only in a piece for which the publishers obtained my indemnification,[33] but in others which followed suit.[34] When I lost count, the number of times this quotation has been repeated was, I think, ten.

But where does the quotation come from? Cast your eye over the Rede Lecture with modest textual attentiveness. You will not find the phrase. It occurs nowhere. Indeed it would be surprising if it did. For I was trying to make a statement of the extremest singularity. No one would elect to make such a statement in plural form. Oddly enough, the English language does not meet the requirements comfortably. 'One dies alone' is not right. I finally had to use a phrase which was clumsy but said what I meant— 'Each of us dies alone'.

This concept, by the way, like so much else in the whole argument, is not original. It has been used in introspective thought, and particularly in introspective religious thought, for centuries. So far as I know, it was said first by Blaise Pascal: *On mourra seul*.

There will be scope for investigations of this kind later: but, I hope, not now. The important thing is to take the personalities, so far as we are able, out of the discussion. In what I am going to write myself I shall try to aim at this.

As I have already said, I think the most useful thing I can now do is to have another look at what I originally wrote: to look at it in the light of what has been said about it, for, against, and at right angles; and to do so with the help of new scientific, sociological and historical knowledge which, as research proceeds, should help, at least on a part of the problem, to provide not an opinion but an answer.

The statements in the lecture were as simple as I could make them. Any statements which have any reference to action must be simple. There is always something wrong, if one is straining to make the commonplace incomprehensible. I hedged the statements round with qualifications and I tried to illustrate some of them. I will now remove the qualifications and the pictures and rephrase the essence of the lecture as quietly as I can.

It is something like this. In our society (that is, advanced western society) we have lost even the pretence of a common culture. Persons educated with the greatest intensity we know can no longer communicate with each other on the plane of their major intellectual concern. This is serious for our creative, intellectual and, above all, our normal life. It is leading us to interpret the past wrongly, to misjudge the present, and to deny our hopes of the future. It is making it difficult or impossible for us to take good action.

I gave the most pointed example of this lack of communication in the shape of two groups of people, representing what I have christened 'the two cultures'. One of these contained the scientists, whose weight, achievement and influence did not need stressing. The other contained the literary intellectuals. I did not mean that literary intellectuals act as the main decision-makers of the western world. I meant that literary intellectuals represent, vocalise, and to some extent shape and predict the mood of the non-scientific culture: they do not make the decisions, but their words seep into the minds of those who do. Between these two groups—the scientists and the literary intellectuals—there is little communication and, instead of fellow-feeling, something like hostility.

This was intended as a description of, or a very crude first approximation to, our existing state of affairs. That it was a state of affairs I passionately disliked, I thought was made fairly clear. Curiously enough, some commentators have assumed that I approved of it; but at this I confess myself defeated, and take refuge in muttering Schiller's helpful line.[35]

To finish this précis. There is, of course, no complete solution. In the conditions of our age, or any age which we can foresee, Renaissance man is not possible. But we can do something. The chief means open to us is education—education mainly in primary and secondary schools, but also in colleges and universities. There is no excuse for letting another generation be as vastly ignorant, or as devoid of understanding and sympathy, as we are ourselves.

§ 3

From the beginning, the phrase 'the two cultures' evoked some protests. The word 'culture' or 'cultures' has been objected to: so, with much more substance, has the number two. (No one, I think, has yet complained about the definite article.)

I must have a word about these verbal points before I come to the more wide-reaching arguments. The term 'culture' in my title has two meanings, both of which are precisely applicable to the theme. First, 'culture' has the sense of the dictionary definition, 'intellectual development, development of the mind'. For many years this definition has carried overtones, often of a deep and ambiguous sort. It happens that few of us can help searching for a refined use of the word: if anyone asks, What is culture? Who is cultured? the needle points, by an extraordinary coincidence, in the direction of ourselves.

But that, though a pleasing example of human frailty, doesn't matter: what does matter is that any refined definition, from Coleridge onwards, applies at least as well (and also as imperfectly) to the development a scientist achieves *in the course of his professional vocation* as to the 'traditional' mental development or any of its offshoots. Coleridge said 'cultivation' where we should say 'culture'—and qualified it as 'the harmonious development of those qualities and faculties which characterise our humanity'.[36] Well, none of us manages that; in plain truth, either of our cultures, whether literary or scientific, only deserves the name of sub-culture. '*Qualities and faculties which characterise our humanity.*' Curiosity about the natural world, the use of symbolic systems of thought, are two of the most precious and the most specifically human of all human qualities. The traditional methods of mental development left them to be starved. So, in reverse, does scientific education starve our verbal faculties—the language of symbols is given splendid play, the language of words is not. On both sides we underestimate the spread of a human being's gifts.

But, if we are to use 'culture' in its refined sense at all, it is only lack of imagination, or possibly blank ignorance, which could deny it to scientists. There is no excuse for such ignorance. A whole body of literature has been built up over a generation, written, incidentally, in some of the most beautiful prose of our time, to demonstrate the intellectual, aesthetic and moral values inherent in the pursuit of science (compare A. N. Whitehead's *Science and the Modern World*, G. H. Hardy's *A Mathematician's Apology*, J. Bronowski's *Science and Human Values*). There are valuable insights scattered all over American and English writing of the last decade—Needham, Toulmin, Price, Piel, Newman, are only a few of the names that come to mind.

In the most lively of all contributions to this subject, a Third Programme feature not yet published, Bronowski deliberately avoided the word 'culture' for either side and chose as his title 'Dialogue between Two World Systems'. For myself, I believe the word is still appropriate and carries its proper meaning to sensible persons. But, while sticking to that word, I want to repeat what was intended to be my main message, but which has somehow got overlaid:

that neither the scientific system of mental development, nor the traditional, is adequate for our potentialities, for the work we have in front of us, for the world in which we ought to begin to live.

The word 'culture' has a second and technical meaning, which I pointed out explicitly in the original lecture. It is used by anthropologists to denote a group of persons living in the same environment, linked by common habits, common assumptions, a common way of life. Thus one talks of a Neanderthal culture, a La Tène culture, a Trobriand Island culture: the term, which is a very useful one, has been applied to groups within our own societies. For me this was a very strong additional reason for selecting the word; it isn't often one gets a word which can be used in two senses, both of which one explicitly intends. For scientists on the one side, literary intellectuals on the other, do in fact exist as cultures within the anthropological scope. There are, as I said before, common attitudes, common standards and patterns of behaviour, common approaches and assumptions. This does not mean that a person within a culture loses his individuality and free will. It does mean that, without knowing it, we are more than we think children of our time, place and training. Let me take two trivial and non-controversial examples. The overwhelming majority of the scientific culture (that is, the group of scientists observed through anthropological eyes) would feel certain, without needing to cogitate or examine their souls, that research was the primary function of a university. This attitude is automatic, it is part of their culture: but it would not be the attitude of such a proportion in the literary culture. On the other hand, the overwhelming majority of the literary culture would feel just as certain that not the slightest censorship of the printed word is, in any circumstances, permissible. This position doesn't have to be reached by individual thought: again it is part of the culture. It is such an unquestioned part, in fact, that the literary intellectuals have got their way more absolutely than, thirty years ago, would have seemed conceivable.

That is enough on 'cultures'. Now for the number Two. Whether this was the best choice, I am much less certain. Right from the start I introduced some qualifying doubts. I will repeat what I said, near the beginning of the lecture.

'The number 2 is a very dangerous number: that is why the dialectic is a dangerous process. Attempts to divide anything into two ought to be regarded with much suspicion. I have thought a long time about going in for further refinements: but in the end I have decided against. I was searching for something a little more than a dashing metaphor, a good deal less than a cultural map: and for those purposes the two cultures is about right, and subtilising any more would bring more disadvantages than it's worth.'

That still seems to me fairly sensible. But I am open to correction, and I have been much impressed by a new feature in the situation, which I will come to in a moment. Before that, however, I ought to mention two lines of argument; one goes happily away into nullity, the other, which I should once have followed myself, can be misleading. The first says, no, there aren't two cultures, there are a hundred and two, or two thousand and two, or any number you like to name. In a sense this is true: but it is also meaningless. Words are always simpler than the brute reality from which they make patterns: if they weren't, discussion and collective action would both be impossible. *Of course* there is sub-division after sub-division within, say, the scientific culture. Theoretical physicists tend to talk only to each other, and, like so many Cabots, to God. Either in scientific politics or open politics, organic chemists much more often than not turn out to be conservative: the reverse is true of biochemists. And so on. Hardy used to say that one could see all these diversities in action round the council table of the Royal Society. But Hardy, who was no respecter either of labels or institutions, would not on that account have said that the Royal Society represented nothing. In fact, its existence is a supreme manifestation or symbol of the scientific culture.[37] This attempt at excessive unsimplicity, the 'two thousand and two cultures' school of thought, crops up whenever anyone makes a proposal which opens up a prospect, however distant, of new action. It involves a skill which all conservative functionaries are masters of, as they

66

ingeniously protect the status quo: it is called 'the technique of the intricate defensive'.

The second line of argument draws, or attempts to draw, a clear line between pure science and technology (which is tending to become a pejorative word). This is a line that once I tried to draw myself:[38] but, though I can still see the reasons, I shouldn't now. The more I have seen of technologists at work, the more untenable the distinction has come to look. If you actually see someone design an aircraft, you find him going through the same experience— aesthetic, intellectual, moral—as though he were setting up an experiment in particle physics.

The scientific process has two motives: one is to understand the natural world, the other is to control it. Either of these motives may be dominant in any individual scientist; fields of science may draw their original impulses from one or the other. Cosmogony for example—the study of the origin and nature of the cosmos—is a pretty pure example of the first class. Medicine is the type specimen of the second. Yet, in all scientific fields, however the work originated, one motive becomes implicit in the other. From medicine, which is a classical technology, men have worked back to 'pure' scientific problems— such as, say, the structure of the haemoglobin molecule. From cosmogony, which seems the most unpractical of all subjects, have come insights into nuclear fission—which, for evil and potentially for good, no one could call an unpractical activity.

This complex dialectic between pure and applied science is one of the deepest problems in scientific history. At present there is much of it which we don't begin to understand. Sometimes the practical need which inspires a wave of invention is brutally obvious. No one has to be told why British, American, German scientists suddenly—at first unknown to each other—made great advances in electronics between 1935 and 1945. It was equally plain that this immensely powerful technological weapon would soon be used in the purest of scientific researches, from astronomy to cybernetics. But what conceivable external stimulus or social correlative set Bolyai, Gauss and Lobachewski—also, in the beginning, unknown to each other—working at the same point in time on non-Euclidean geometry, apparently one of the most abstract of all fields of the conceptual imagination? It is going to be difficult to find a satisfying answer. But we may make it impossible, if we start by assuming a difference in kind between pure science and applied.

§ 4

So the phrase 'the two cultures' still seems appropriate for the purpose I had in mind. I now think, however, that I should have stressed more heavily that I was speaking as an Englishman, from experience drawn mainly from English society. I did in fact say this, and I said also that this cultural divide seems at its sharpest in England. I now realise that I did not emphasise it enough.

In the United States, for example, the divide is nothing like so unbridgeable. There are pockets of the literary culture, influenced by the similar culture in England, which are as extreme in resisting communication and in ceasing to communicate: but that isn't generally true over the literary culture as a whole, much less over the entire intellectual society. And, just because the divide is not so deep, just because the situation is not accepted as a fact of life, far more active steps are being taken to improve it. This is an interesting example of one of the laws of social change: change doesn't happen when things are at their worst, but when they are looking up. So it is at Yale and Princeton and Michigan and California, that scientists of world standing are talking to non-specialised classes: at M.I.T. and Cal. Tech. where students of the sciences are receiving a serious humane education. In the last few years, all over the country, a visitor cannot help being astonished by the resilience and inventiveness of American higher education—ruefully so, if he happens to be an Englishman.[39]

I think also that writing as an Englishman made me insensitive to something which may, within a few years, propel the argument in another direction or which conceivably may already have started to do just that. I have been increasingly impressed by a body of intellectual opinion, forming itself, without

69

organisation, without any kind of lead or conscious direction, under the surface of this debate. This is the new feature I referred to a little earlier. This body of opinion seems to come from intellectual persons in a variety of fields—social history, sociology, demography, political science, economics, government (in the American academic sense), psychology, medicine, and social arts such as architecture. It seems a mixed bag: but there is an inner consistency. All of them are concerned with how human beings are living or have lived—and concerned, not in terms of legend, but of fact. I am not implying that they agree with each other, but in their approach to cardinal problems—such as the human effects of the scientific revolution, which is the fighting point of this whole affair—they display, at the least, a family resemblance.

I ought, I see now, to have expected this. I haven't much excuse for not doing so. I have been in close intellectual contact with social historians most of my life: they have influenced me a good deal: their recent researches were the basis for a good many of my statements. But nevertheless I was slow to observe the development of what, in the terms of our formulae, is becoming something like a third culture. I might have been quicker if I had not been the prisoner of my English upbringing, conditioned to be suspicious of any but the established intellectual disciplines, unreservedly at home only with the 'hard' subjects. For this I am sorry.

It is probably too early to speak of a third culture

already in existence. But I am now convinced that this is coming. When it comes, some of the difficulties of communication will at last be softened: for such a culture has, just to do its job, to be on speaking terms with the scientific one. Then, as I said, the focus of this argument will be shifted, in a direction which will be more profitable to us all.

There are signs that this is happening. Some social historians, as well as being on speaking terms with scientists, have felt bound to turn their attention to the literary intellectuals, or more exactly to some manifestations of the literary culture at its extreme. Concepts such as the 'organic community' or the nature of pre-industrial society or the scientific revolution are being dealt with, under the illumination of the knowledge of the last ten years. These new examinations are of great importance for our intellectual and moral health.

Since they touch on the parts of my lecture on which I have the deepest feelings, I shall revert to them once again in the next section. After that I shall leave them in the hands of those professionally qualified to speak.

One word about another passage where I showed bad judgment. In my account of the lack of communication between the two cultures, I didn't exaggerate: if anything I understated the case, as has been proved by subsequent pieces of fieldwork.[40] Yet I have regretted that I used as my test question about scientific literacy, *What do you know of the*

*Second Law of Thermodynamics?* It is, in fact, a good question. Many physical scientists would agree that it is perhaps the most pointed question. This law is one of the greatest depth and generality: it has its own sombre beauty: like all the major scientific laws, it evokes reverence. There is, of course, no value in a non-scientist just knowing it by the rubric in an encyclopedia. It needs understanding, which can't be attained unless one has learnt some of the language of physics. That understanding ought to be part of a common twentieth-century culture—as Lord Cherwell once said, more astringently than I have done, in the House of Lords. Nevertheless I wish that I had chosen a different example. I had forgotten—like a playwright who has lost touch with his audience— that the law is called by what to most people is an unfamiliar, and therefore a funny, name. To be honest, I had forgotten how funny the unfamiliar is—I ought to have remembered the jocularity with which the English greeted the Russian patronymics in Chekhov, roaring their heads off each time they heard Fyodor Ilyich or Lyubov Andreievna, expressing their blissful ignorance of a formal nomenclature both more courteous and more human than their own.

So I got a laugh: but again, like an incompetent playwright, I got a laugh in the wrong place. I should now treat the matter differently, and I should put forward a branch of science which ought to be a requisite in the common culture, certainly for anyone now at school. This branch of science at present goes by the name of molecular biology. Is that funny? I think that possibly it is already well enough domesticated. Through a whole set of lucky chances, this study is ideally suited to fit into a new model of education. It is fairly self-contained. It begins with the analysis of crystal structure, itself a subject aesthetically beautiful and easily comprehended. It goes on to the application of these methods to molecules which have literally a vital part in our own existence—molecules of proteins, nucleic acids: molecules immensely large (by molecular standards) and which turn out to be of curious shapes, for nature, when interested in what we call life, appears to have a taste for the rococo. It includes the leap of genius by which Crick and Watson snatched at the structure of DNA and so taught us the essential lesson about our genetic inheritance.

Unlike thermodynamics, the subject does not involve serious conceptual difficulties. In fact, in terms of concept, it doesn't reach so deep, and it is for other reasons that it has a first claim upon us. It needs very little mathematics to understand. There are few parts of the hard sciences of which one can understand so much without mathematical training. What one needs most of all is a visual and three-dimensional imagination, and it is a study where painters and sculptors could be instantaneously at home.

It exemplifies, with extreme neatness, some of the characteristics of the whole scientific culture, its subdivisions and its community. Exponents of the 'two thousand and two cultures' school of thought will be glad to hear that only a handful of people in the world—five hundred?—would be competent to follow in detail each step of the process by which, say, Perutz and Kendrew finally disentangled the structure of the haem proteins. After all, Perutz was at haemoglobin, on and off, for twenty-five years. But any scientist with the patience to learn could get instructed in those processes, and any scientist knows it. The great majority of scientists can acquire an adequate working knowledge of what the results mean. All scientists without exception accept the results. It is a nice demonstration of the scientific culture at work.

I have said that the ideas in this branch of science are not as physically deep, or of such universal physical significance, as those in the Second Law. That is true. The Second Law is a generalisation which covers the cosmos. This new study deals only with microscopic parts of the cosmos, which may—no one knows—exist only on this earth: but since those microscopic parts happen to be connected with biological life, they are of importance to each of us. It is very hard to write about this importance. It is better, I think, to take a self-denying ordinance and let the researches of the next ten years make it plain. But here is a statement which is not seriously controversial. This branch of science is likely to affect the way in which *men think of themselves* more profoundly than any scientific advance since Darwin's—and probably more so than Darwin's.

That seems a sufficient reason why the next generation should learn about it. The Church recognises
invincible ignorance: but here the ignorance is not,
or need not be, invincible. This study could be grafted
into any of our educational systems, at high school
or college levels, without artificiality and without
strain. I dare say that, as usual, this is an idea which
is already floating around the world, and that, as I
write this paragraph, some American college has
already laid on the first course.

## § 5

Major scentific breakthroughs, and in particular
those as closely connected to human flesh and bone
as this one in molecular biology, or even more,
another which we may expect in the nature of the
higher nervous system, are bound to touch both
our hopes and our resignations. That is: ever since
men began to think introspectively about themselves,
they have made guesses, and sometimes had profound
intuitions, about those parts of their own nature which
seemed to be predestined. It is possible that within a
generation some of these guesses will have been
tested against exact knowledge. No one can predict
what such an intellectual revolution will mean: but
I believe that one of the consequences will be to make
us feel not less but more responsible towards our
brother men.

It was for this reason among others that, in the original lecture, I drew a distinction between the individual condition and the social condition. In doing so, I stressed the solitariness, the ultimate tragedy, at the core of each individual life; and this has worried a good many who found the rest of the statement acceptable. It is very hard, of course, to subdue the obsessions of one's own temperament; this specific note creeps into a good deal of what I have written, as Alfred Kazin has shrewdly pointed out:[41] it is not an accident that my novel sequence is called *Strangers and Brothers*. Nevertheless, this distinction, however it is drawn, is imperative, unless we are going to sink into the facile social pessimism of our time, unless we are going to settle into our own egocentric chill.

So I will try to make the statement without much emphasis of my own. We should most of us agree, I think, that in the individual life of each of us there is much that, in the long run, one cannot do anything about. Death is a fact—one's own death, the deaths of those one loves. There is much that makes one suffer which is irremediable: one struggles against it all the way, but there is an irremediable residue left. These are facts: they will remain facts as long as man remains man. This is part of the individual condition: call it tragic, comic, absurd, or, like some of the best and bravest of people, shrug it off.

But it isn't all. One looks outside oneself to other lives, to which one is bound by love, affection,

76

loyalty, obligation: each of those lives has the same irremediable components as one's own; but there are also components that one can help, or that can give one help. It is in this tiny extension of the personality, it is in this seizing on the possibilities of hope, that we become more fully human: it is a way to improve the quality of one's life: it is, for oneself, the beginning of the social condition.

Finally, one can try to understand the condition of lives, not close to one's own, which one cannot know face to face. Each of these lives—that is, the lives of one's fellow human beings—again has limits of irremediability like one's own. Each of them has needs, some of which can be met: the totality of all is the social condition.

We cannot know as much as we should about the social condition all over the world. But we can know, we do know, two most important things. First we can meet the harsh facts of the flesh, on the level where all of us are, or should be, one. We know that the vast majority, perhaps two-thirds, of our fellow men are living in the immediate presence of illness and premature death; their expectation of life is half of ours, most are under-nourished, many are near to starving, many starve. Each of these lives is afflicted by suffering, different from that which is intrinsic in the individual condition. But this suffering is unnecessary and can be lifted. This is the second important thing which we know—or, if we don't know it, there is no excuse or absolution for us.

We cannot avoid the realisation that applied science has made it possible to remove unnecessary suffering from a billion individual human lives—to remove suffering of a kind, which, in our own privileged society, we have largely forgotten, suffering so elementary that it is not genteel to mention it. For example, we *know* how to heal many of the sick: to prevent children dying in infancy and mothers in childbirth: to produce enough food to alleviate hunger: to throw up a minimum of shelter: to ensure that there aren't so many births that our other efforts are in vain. All this we *know* how to do.

It does not require one additional scientific discovery, though new scientific discoveries must help us. It depends on the spread of the scientific revolution all over the world. There is no other way. For most human beings, this is the point of hope. It will certainly happen. It may take longer than the poor will peacefully accept. How long it takes, and the fashion in which it is done, will be a reflex of the quality of our lives, especially of the lives of those of us born lucky: as most in the western world were born.[42] When it is achieved, then our consciences will be a little cleaner; and those coming after us will at least be able to think that the elemental needs of others aren't a daily reproach to any sentient person, that for the first time some genuine dignity has come upon us all.

Man doesn't live by bread alone—yes, that has been said often enough in the course of these discussions.

It has been said occasionally with a lack of imagination, a provincialism, that makes the mind boggle: for it is not a remark that one of us in the western world can casually address to most Asians, to most of our fellow human beings, in the world as it now exists. But we can, we should, say it to ourselves. For we know how, once the elemental needs are satisfied, we do not find it easy to do something worthy and satisfying with our lives. Probably it will never be easy. Conceivably men in the future, if they are as lucky as we are now, will struggle with our existential discontents, or new ones of their own. They may, like some of us, try—through sex or drink or drugs—to intensify the sensational life. Or they may try to improve the quality of their lives, through an extension of their responsibilities, a deepening of the affections and the spirit, in a fashion which, though we can aim at it for ourselves and our own societies, we can only dimly perceive.

But, though our perception may be dim, it isn't dim enough to obscure one truth: that one mustn't despise the elemental needs, when one has been granted them and others have not. To do so is not to display one's superior spirituality. It is simply to be inhuman, or more exactly anti-human.

Here, in fact, was what I intended to be the centre of the whole argument. Before I wrote the lecture I thought of calling it 'The Rich and the Poor', and I rather wish that I hadn't changed my mind.

The scientific revolution is the only method by

which most people can gain the primal things (years of life, freedom from hunger, survival for children)—the primal things which we take for granted and which have in reality come to us through having had our own scientific revolution not so long ago. Most people want these primal things. Most people, wherever they are being given a chance, are rushing into the scientific revolution.

To misunderstand this position is to misunderstand both the present and the future. It simmers beneath the surface of world politics. Though the form of politics may look the same, its content is being altered as the scientific revolution pours in. We have not been as quick as we should to draw the right consequences, very largely because of the division of the cultures. It has been hard for politicians and administrators to grasp the practical truth of what scientists were telling them. But now it is beginning to be accepted. It is often accepted most easily by men of affairs, whatever their political sympathies, engineers, or priests, or doctors, all those who have a strong comradely physical sympathy for other humans. If others can get the primal things—yes, that is beyond argument; that is simply good.

Curiously enough, there are many who would call themselves liberals and yet who are antipathetic to this change. Almost as though sleepwalking they drift into an attitude which, to the poor of the world, is a denial of all human hope. This attitude, which misinterprets both the present and the future, seems to be connected with a similar misinterpretation of the past. It is on this point that representatives of the putative third culture have been speaking with trenchancy.

The argument is about the first wave of the scientific revolution, the transformation which we call the industrial revolution, and it is occupied with questions about what, in the most elementary human terms, life was like in pre-industrial as compared with industrial society. We can gain some insights, of course, from the present world, which is a vast sociological laboratory in which one can observe all kinds of society from the neolithic to the advanced industrial. We are also now accumulating substantial evidence of our own past.

When I made some remarks about the industrial revolution, I had imagined that the findings of recent research in social history were better known. Otherwise I should have documented what I said: but that seemed like documenting a platitude. Did anyone think that, in the primal terms in which I have just been discussing the poor countries of the present world, our ancestors' condition was so very different? Or that the industrial revolution had not brought us in three or four generations to a state entirely new in the harsh, unrecorded continuity of poor men's lives? I couldn't believe it. I knew, of course, the force of nostalgia, myth, and plain snobbery. In all families, at all times, there are stories of blessed existences, just before one's childhood: there were in my own.

Myth—I ought to have remembered what Malinowski taught us, that people believe their myths as fact. I certainly ought to have remembered that, when anyone is asked what he would have been in a previous incarnation, he nominates—if he is modest—something like a Jacobean cleric or an eighteenth-century squire. He wouldn't have been any such thing. The overwhelming probability is that he would have been a peasant. If we want to talk about our ancestors, that is whence we came.

I was at fault, I suppose, in not trying to be more persuasive against these kinds of resistance. Anyway, there is no need for me to say much more. There are plenty of scholars professionally concerned with pre-industrial social history. Now we know something of the elemental facts of the lives and deaths of peasants and agricultural labourers in seventeenth- and eighteenth-century England and France. They are not comfortable facts. J. H. Plumb, in one of his attacks on the teaching of a pretty-pretty past, has written: 'No one in his senses would choose to have been born in a previous age unless he could be certain that he would have been born into a prosperous family, that he would have enjoyed extremely good health, and that he could have accepted stoically the death of the majority of his children.'

It is worth anyone's while—in fact no one ought to escape the experience—to study the results which the French demographers have obtained in the last decade. In the seventeenth and eighteenth centuries, parish registers in France were kept with great accuracy, much more commonly so than in England —births, marriages and deaths the only tiny records, the only traces, of so many human lives. These records are now being analysed all over France.[43] They tell a story which can be duplicated in Asian (or Latin American) communities today.

In the dry but appallingly eloquent language of statistics, the historians explain to us that, in eighteenth-century French villages, the median age of marriage was higher than the median age of death. The *average* length of life was perhaps a third of ours, and appreciably less, because of the deaths in childbirth, for women than for men (*it is only quite recently, and in lucky countries, that women, on the average, have had a chance of living as long as men*). The greater part of entire communities[44] died of starvation, which appears to have been a common occurrence.

Though English records are nothing like so complete, Peter Laslett and his collaborators have discovered some late seventeenth-century registers,[45] and are actively extending their researches. The same stark conclusions stand out—except that in England there is as yet no proof of periodical famine, though it was endemic among the Scottish poor.

There is a mass of other evidence, from many kinds of provenance, all pointing in the same direction. In the light of it, no one should feel it seriously possible to talk about a pre-industrial Eden, from which our ancestors were, by the wicked machinations of applied science, brutally expelled. When and where was this Eden? Will someone who hankers after the myth tell us where he believes it was located, not in terms of wishful fancy, but in place and time, in historical and geographical fact? Then the social historians can examine the case and there can be a respectable discussion.

The present position is not respectable. One can't talk or teach false social history when the professionals are proving the falsity under one's eyes. Yet, as Plumb has publicly protested, what he calls 'this nonsense' is being taught. To anyone educated in an exact discipline it all seems very peculiar, almost as though reading itself had gone out of fashion as an activity, certainly the reading of any evidence which contradicts the stereotypes of fifty years ago. It is rather as though the teachers of physics had ignored the quantum theory and had gone on, year after year, teaching precisely those radiation laws which the quantum theory had been brought in to replace. And teaching them with that special insistence which strains the voices of priests of a dying religion.

It is important for the pre-industrial believers to confront the social historians. Then we can get a basis of fact accepted. One can teach a myth: but when the myth is seen as fact, and when the fact is disproved, the myth becomes a lie. No one can teach a lie.

I have restricted myself to primal things. It seems to me better that people should live rather than die:

that they shouldn't be hungry: that they shouldn't have to watch their children die. Here, if anywhere, we are members one of another. If we are not members one of another, if we have no sympathy at this elemental level, then we have no human concern at all, and any pretence of a higher kind of sympathy is a mockery. Fortunately most of us are not so affectless as that.

Anyone who has had a physical misfortune knows that many acquaintances who would feel for him in no other circumstances, genuinely feel for him in this one. The sympathy is visceral: it is a sign that we cannot deny our common humanity.

Therefore the social condition is with us, we are part of it, we cannot deny it. Millions of individual lives, in some lucky countries like our own, have, by one gigantic convulsion of applied science over the last hundred and fifty years, been granted some share of the primal things. Billions of individual lives, over the rest of the world, will be granted or will seize the same. This is the indication of time's arrow. It is by far the greatest revolution our kind has known. We have been living through rapid change for three or four generations. Now the change is going faster. It is bound to go a great deal faster still. This is the condition in which we are both agents and spectators. Our response to it affects, and often determines, what we like and dislike in our world, what action we take, the nature of the art we value or practise, the nature of our appreciation of science. It determines also, I fancy, the way in which some straightforward proposals about education, intended to be simple and practical, have been made the jumping-off point for a debate on first and last things.

## § 6

We are only just beginning to live with the industrial-scientific revolution; we have taken the first positive steps to control it, to compensate for its losses as well as to absorb its gains. The modern industrial communities of, say, Northern Italy or Sweden, are qualitatively different from those which first accumulated in Lancashire or New England. The whole process has not yet dived into our imaginative understanding. We who comment about it stand outside: socially in that most dangerous of positions, one tiny step more privileged than those who are taking part.

One point, however, is clear; those who are taking part have never paid one instant's attention to the lookers-on who would like them to reject industrialisation. As I said in the original lecture, this is a manifest fact in all societies all over the world. It is these witnesses whom we ought to consult, not those of us who are one step luckier, who think we know what is good for them.

The primary reason for their enthusiasm, which was set out in the last section, was so strong that men would need no others. But I believe there are others, quite deep in the individual's intuitive life, which impel most young people to elect for living in towns whenever they have a free choice, and others again which impel nearly all unprivileged people to prefer a highly organised society to one based on simple power relations.

The first class of reasons is obvious enough, and does not need explication: have you ever been young? The second is a little more subtle. Perhaps I can illustrate it by, so to speak, an example in reverse. I am reminded of D. H. Lawrence[46] reflecting on an anecdote in Dana's *Two Years Before the Mast*. The passage is a very long one, and should be read in full: it is about Dana feeling revolted when the captain of the ship has a sailor called Sam flogged. Lawrence denounces Dana for being revolted: Lawrence approves.

Master and servant—or master and man relationship is, essentially, a polarized flow, like love. It is a circuit of vitalism which flows between master and man and forms a very precious nourishment to each, and keeps both in a state of subtle, quivering, vital equilibrium. Deny it as you like, it is so. But once you *abstract* both master and man, and make them both serve an *idea*: production, wage, efficiency, and so on: so that each looks on himself as an instrument performing a certain repeated evolution, then you have changed the vital, quivering circuit of master and man into a mechanical machine unison. Just another way of life: or anti-life.

. . . . . . . . .

87

Flogging.

You have a Sam, a fat slow fellow, who has got slower and more slovenly as the weeks wear on. You have a master who has grown more irritable in his authority. Till Sam becomes simply wallowing in his slackness, makes your gorge rise. And the master is on red hot iron.

Now these two men, Captain and Sam, are there in a very unsteady equilibrium of command and obedience. A polarized flow. Definitely polarized.

.    .    .    .    .    .    .    .    .

'Tie up that lousy swine!' roars the enraged Captain.

And whack! Whack! down on the bare back of that sloucher Sam comes the cat.

What does it do? By Jove, it goes like ice-cold water into his spine. Down those lashes runs the current of the Captain's rage, right into the blood and into the toneless ganglia of Sam's voluntary system. Crash! Crash! runs the lightning flame, right into the cores of the living nerves.

And the living nerves respond. They start to vibrate. They brace up. The blood begins to go quicker. The nerves begin to recover their vividness. It is their tonic. The man Sam has a new clear day of intelligence, and a smarty back. The Captain has a new relief, a new ease in his authority, and a sore heart.

There is a new equilibrium, and a fresh start. The *physical* intelligence of a Sam is restored, the turgidity is relieved from the veins of the Captain.

It is a natural form of human coition, interchange.

It is good for Sam to be flogged. It is good, on this occasion, for the Captain to have Sam flogged. I say so.

This reflection is the exact opposite of that which would occur to anyone who had never held, or

88

expected to hold, the right end of the whip—which means most of the poor of the world, all the unprivileged, the teeming majority of our fellow men. Such a man may not be lazy like Sam: nevertheless he doesn't like being in another's power. He doesn't take this Rousseauish view of the virtue of the direct expression of emotion, or 'the circuit of vitalism',[47] or 'the blood contact of life'. *He* has suffered others' tempers, at the receiving end. *He* is not romantic at all about the beauties of the master-and-man relation: that illusion is open only to those who have climbed one step up and are hanging on by their fingernails. *He* knows, through the long experience of the poor, what the real condition of direct power is like—if you want it treated with ultimate humanity and wisdom read Bruno Bettelheim's *The Informed Heart*.

So, with singular unanimity the unprivileged have elected for societies where they are as far away as possible from the Captain-Sam situation—which, of course, highly articulated societies are. Trade unions, collective dealing, the entire apparatus of modern industry—they may be maddening to those who have never had the experience of the poor, but they stand like barbed wire against the immediate assertion of the individual will. And, as soon as the poor began to escape from their helplessness, the assertion of the individual will was the first thing they refused to take.

# § 7

With the scientific revolution going on around us, what has our literature made of it? This is a topic which I mentioned in the lecture, but about which almost everything remains to be said. Probably some sort of examination will be produced in the next few years. For myself, I shall be glad to get this part of the controversy into better perspective. I will make one or two comments to show some of my present thinking: to those, if I believe I can add something useful, I shall in due course return.

Let me begin some distance off the point. It happens that, of all novelists, Dostoevsky is the one I know the best. When I was twenty, I thought *The Brothers Karamazov* was by a long way the greatest novel ever written, and its author the most magnificent of novelists. Gradually my enthusiasm became more qualified: as I grew older I found Tolstoy meaning more to me. But Dostoevsky is to this day one of the novelists I most admire: besides Tolstoy there seem to me only two or three others who can live in the same light.

This confession of personal taste is not so irrelevant as it seems. Of the great novelists Dostoevsky is the one whose social attitudes are most explicitly revealed —not in his novels, where he is ambiguous, but in the *Writer's Diary* which he published once a month during the years 1876–80, when he was in his fifties and near the peak of his fame. In the *Diary*, which was produced as a single-handed effort, he gave answers to readers' problems of the heart (the advice was almost always practical and wise), but he devoted most of his space to political propaganda, to passionate and increasingly unambiguous expression of his own prescripts for action.

They are pretty horrifying, even after ninety years. He was virulently anti-semitic: he prayed for war: he was against any kind of emancipation at any time; he was a fanatical supporter of the autocracy, and an equally fanatical opponent of any improvement in the lives of the common people (on the grounds that they loved their suffering and were ennobled by it). He was in fact the supreme reactionary: other writers since have aspired to this condition, but no one has had his force of nature and his psychological complexity. It is worth noting that he wasn't speaking in a vacuum; this wasn't like Lawrence banging away with exhortations, some of them similarly regrettable.[48] Dostoevsky lived in society; his diary was influential, and acted as the voice of the ultra-conservatives, to whom he himself in secret acted as a kind of psychological adviser.

Thus I have not a social idea in common with him. If I had been his contemporary, he would have tried to get me put in gaol. And yet I know him to be a great writer, and I know that, not with detached admiration, but with a feeling much warmer. So do present day Russians know it. Their response is much the same as mine. Posterity is in the long run forgiving, if a writer is good enough.[49] No one could call Dostoevsky an agreeable character, and he did finite harm. But compare him with the generous and open-hearted Chernyshevsky, who had a sense of the future of the world flat contrary to Dostoevsky's, and whose foresight has turned out nearer to the truth. The goodwill, the social passion of Chernyshevsky have kept his memory fresh: but posterity ignores wrong or wicked judgments, and it is Dostoevsky's books which stay alive. *What is to be done?* or *The Brothers Karamazov*?—posterity, if it knows anything of the two personal histories, gives a grim, reluctant, sarcastic smile, and knows which it has to choose.

It will be the same in the future. Persons ignorant of the nature of change, antagonistic to the scientific revolution which will impose social changes such as none of us can foresee, often think and talk and hope as though all literary judgments for ever will be made from the same viewpoint as that of contemporary London or New York: as though we had reached a kind of social plateau which is the final resting-ground of literate man. That, of course, is absurd. The social matrix will change, education will change, with greater acceleration than it did between the time of the *Edinburgh Review* and the *Partisan Review*: judgments will change. But it is not necessary to go to extremes of subjectivity. Major writers are able to survive the invention of new categories; they resist the influence of ideologies, including most of all their own. As we read, our imaginations stretch wider than our beliefs. If we construct mental boxes to shut out what won't fit, then we make ourselves meaner.[50] Among near contemporaries whom I admire, I could mention Bernard Malamud, Robert Graves, William Golding: it would be a tough job to assimilate these three into any scheme or ideology, literary or non-literary, which could conceivably be associated with me. So, in a future society, different from ours, some of the great literary names of our time will still be venerated. This will be true of the major talents in the 'movement' of which Dostoevsky was a distant and eccentric precursor and which lasted, as the literature of the western *avant-garde*, down until the very recent past.

The writers who have taken part in this movement are nowadays often called 'modernists' or 'moderns'; the terms may seem a little odd for a school which began well back in the nineteenth century and which has left scarcely any active practitioners; but literary terms are odd, and if we don't like these we can think of them as terms of art, like the adjectives in New College or *art nouveau*. Anyway, we all know what is meant: there would be fair agreement on some of the representative names—Laforgue, Henry James, Dujardin, Dorothy Richardson, T. S. Eliot, Yeats, Pound, Hulme, Joyce, Lawrence, Sologub, Andrei Bely,[51] Virginia Woolf, Wyndham Lewis, Gide, Musil, Kafka, Benn, Valéry, Faulkner, Beckett.

According to taste, and according to one's funda-mental attitude to the implications of modernism, one adds names or subtracts them.[52] Thus Lukács, by far the most powerful of its antagonists, would not include Thomas Mann: while Trilling, one of its committed defenders, certainly would. And so on.

We should nearly all agree that the modernist movement includes a majority, though not all, of the high talents in western literature over a longish period. We should further agree that the individual works of individual writers have an existence of their own; and that the greatest of the modernists' creations will, like Dostoevsky's, swim above the underswell of argument in a changing culture. But about what the movement means in social terms (that is, the social roots from which it grew and its effects upon society), its meaning in the here-and-now of our divided culture, and its influence in the future—here there is a disagreement which can't be glossed over and which may continue after most of us are dead.

There have recently appeared three interesting texts: Lionel Trilling's *The Modern Element in Modern Literature*,[53] Stephen Spender's *The Struggle of the Modern*,[54] Georg Lukács's *The Meaning of Contemporary Realism*.[55] The first striking thing is that, when they are talking of modernism and modern literature, they are talking of what is recognisably the same thing. They value it differently: their formal analysis is different: but, behind all that, the essence to which they are responding is the same.

The confrontation of Lukács and Trilling is picturesque. Each is a very clever man, and clever in somewhat the same fashion. Each brings by design to literary criticism a range of equipment from non-literary disciplines: Lukács from philosophy and economics, Trilling from Freudian psychology. They often give the common impression of being unempirical: when they try to be empirical they have a tendency to overdo it. On modernism, Lukács is temperately and courteously anti, Trilling devotedly pro. In a long and sustained analysis of modernism, Lukács sees its characteristic features as rejection of narrative objectivity: dissolution of the personality: ahistoricity: static view of the human condition (meaning by this mainly what I have called the social condition).

Trilling's views are familiar to most of us. In his recent essay there is an explicit passage:

The author of *The Magic Mountain* once said that all his work could be understood as an effort to free himself from the middle class and this, of course, will serve to describe the intention of all modern literature . . . the end is not freedom from the middle class but freedom from society itself. I venture to say that the idea of losing oneself up to the point of self-destruction, of surrendering oneself to experience without regard to self-interest or morality, escaping wholly from the societal bonds, is an 'element' somewhere in the mind of every modern person who dares to think of what Arnold in his unaffected Victorian way called the 'fullness of spiritual perfection'.

Reading these closely argued, deeply felt and often moving essays one after the other, that is, Lukács's and

95

Trilling's, one has a curious sense of *déjà vu*. Aren't the two insights, which look so different, seeing the same phenomenon? One approves, the other disapproves, and yet there is a link. They might disagree about the social causes of modernism—but each is too subtle to think that these are simple. As Harry Levin has demonstrated,[56] the social origins of classical nineteenth-century realism are more complex than we used to think.

Lukács and Trilling are describing what has happened. The descriptions under the surface often run together. For Trilling's 'freedom from society' presupposes a static view of society. It is the romantic conception of the artist carried to its extreme. And the romantic conception of the artist only has full meaning if there is a social cushion, unaffected by change, unaffected by the scientific revolution, to fall back on. Such an attitude, such a desire, can lead to turning the original dichotomy on its head and taking an optimistic view of one's individual condition and a pessimistic view of the social one. Trilling would not do this, of course: he is too serious a man. But it is a temptation characteristic of the worst-spirited of modernist literature.

I find myself asking a question. It is not a rhetorical question, and I don't know the answer. It would be a satisfaction to know it. The question is this: how far is it possible to share the hopes of the scientific revolution, the modest difficult hopes for other human lives, and at the same time participate without qualification in the kind of literature which has just been defined?

## § 8

Finally, it has been said of the original lecture that it is oblivious of politics. At first sight, this seems strange; for I have written, both in novels and essays, more about politics, in particular 'closed' politics (that is, the way decisions are really taken in power-groups, as contrasted with the way they are supposed to be taken), than most people of our time. But in fact this species of criticism is not as strange as it seems; for those who have uttered it mean something a good deal different from what the overt words convey. That is, they mean by 'politics' something more limited than most of us can accept, and something which is, in my view, profoundly dangerous. They mean, to be brutal, by 'politics' the waging of the cold war. Their criticism amounts to saying that I did not relate the lecture to the cold war, as it was being waged in 1959: or, more sinister still, that I did not accept the cold war as the prime absolute of our age, and of all ages to come.

Of course I didn't. Not in 1959, nor for a good many years before that. It seemed to me that nearly every indication, human, economic, above all technological, pointed the other way. If one knew a little about military technology, it was likely, oddly enough, not only to make the dangers appear sharper, but also the possibility of hope: for it was fairly clear that the discontinuities in military technology could not possibly leave the cold war untouched for long. It was *that* kind of politics, simmering under the surface of the open formulations with which I was concerned, and on the strength of which I made judgments which were totally unlike those of my critics. Some of mine were wrong: in the Rede Lecture I much over-estimated the speed of Chinese industrialisation. But the more significant ones, now that time has passed and we can check some of our guesses, I see no reason to change.

This leads me to the major theme of what I set out to say. Let me try again to make myself clear. It is dangerous to have two cultures which can't or don't communicate. In a time when science is determining much of our destiny, that is, whether we live or die, it is dangerous in the most practical terms. Scientists can give bad advice[57] and decision-makers can't know whether it is good or bad. On the other hand, scientists in a divided culture provide a knowledge of some potentialities which is theirs alone. All this makes the political process more complex, and in some ways more dangerous, than we should be prepared to tolerate for long, either for the purposes of avoiding disasters, or for fulfilling—what is waiting as a challenge to our conscience and goodwill—a definable social hope.

At present we are making do in our half-educated

fashion, struggling to hear messages, obviously of great importance, as though listening to a foreign language in which one only knows a few words. Sometimes, and perhaps often, the logic of applied science is modifying or shaping the political process itself. This has happened over nuclear tests, where we have been lucky enough to see, what hasn't been common in our time, a triumph for human sense. The triumph might have come sooner, if the logic of applied science had been as much at educated persons' disposal as the logic of language. But still, let's not minimise our triumphs. The worst doesn't always happen, as a friend said to me in the summer of 1940. I am beginning to believe that we shall escape or circumvent the greater dangers with which science has confronted us. If I wrote the lecture again now, there would still be anxiety in it, but less dread.

Escaping the dangers of applied science is one thing. Doing the simple and manifest good which applied science has put in our power is another, more difficult, more demanding of human qualities, and in the long run far more enriching to us all. It will need energy, self-knowledge, new skills. It will need new perceptions into both closed and open politics.

In the original lecture, as now, I was isolating only one small corner of the situation: I was talking primarily to educators and those being educated, about something which we all understand and which is within our grasp. Changes in education will not, by themselves, solve our problems: but without those changes we shan't even realise what the problems are.

Changes in education are not going to produce miracles. The division of our culture is making us more obtuse than we need be: we can repair communications to some extent: but, as I have said before, we are not going to turn out men and women who understand as much of our world as Piero della Francesca did of his, or Pascal, or Goethe. With good fortune, however, we can educate a large proportion of our better minds so that they are not ignorant of imaginative experience, both in the arts and in science, nor ignorant either of the endowments of applied science, of the remediable suffering of most of their fellow humans, and of the responsibilities which, once they are seen, cannot be denied.

# NOTES

1 'The Two Cultures', *New Statesman*, 6 October 1956.

2 This lecture was delivered to a Cambridge audience, and so I used some points of reference which I did not need to explain. G. H. Hardy, 1877–1947, was one of the most distinguished pure mathematicians of his time, and a picturesque figure in Cambridge both as a young don and on his return in 1931 to the Sadleirian Chair of Mathematics.

3 I said a little more about this connection in *The Times Literary Supplement*, 'Challenge to the Intellect', 15 August 1958. I hope some day to carry the analysis further.

4 It would be more accurate to say that, for literary reasons, we felt the prevailing literary modes were useless to us. We were, however, reinforced in that feeling when it occurred to us that those prevailing modes went hand in hand with social attitudes either wicked, or absurd, or both.

5 An analysis of the schools from which Fellows of the Royal Society come tells its own story. The distribution is markedly different from that of, for example, members of the Foreign Service or Queen's Counsel.

6 Compare George Orwell's *1984*, which is the strongest possible wish that the future should not exist, with J. D. Bernal's *World Without War*.

7 *Subjective*, in contemporary technological jargon, means 'divided according to subjects'. *Objective* means 'directed towards an object'. *Philosophy* means

'general intellectual approach or attitude' (for example, a scientist's 'philosophy of guided weapons' might lead him to propose certain kinds of 'objective research'). A 'progressive' job means one with possibilities of promotion.

8 Almost all college High Tables contain Fellows in both scientific and non-scientific subjects.

9 He took the examination in 1905.

10 It is, however, true to say that the compact nature of the managerial layers of English society—the fact that 'everyone knows everyone else'—means that scientists and non-scientists do in fact know each other as people more easily than in most countries. It is also true that a good many leading politicians and administrators keep up lively intellectual and artistic interests to a much greater extent, so far as I can judge, than is the case in the U.S. These are both among our assets.

11 I tried to compare American, Soviet and English education in 'New Minds for the New World', *New Statesman*, 6 September 1956.

12 The best, and almost the only, book on the subject.

13 It developed very fast. An English commission of inquiry into industrial productivity went over to the United States as early as 1865.

14 It is reasonable for intellectuals to prefer to live in the eighteenth-century streets of Stockholm rather than in Vallingby. I should myself. But it is not reasonable for them to obstruct other Vállingbys being built.

15 It is worth remembering that there must have been similar losses—spread over a much longer period—when men changed from the hunting and food gathering life to agriculture. For some, it must have been a genuine spiritual impoverishment.

**16** This is not quite exact. In the states where higher education is most completely developed, for example, Wisconsin, about 95 per cent of children attend High School up to eighteen.

**17** The U.S. is a complex and plural society, and the standards of colleges vary very much more than those of our universities. Some college standards are very high. Broadly, I think the generalisation is fair.

**18** The number of engineers graduating per year in the United States is declining fairly sharply. I have not heard an adequate explanation for this.

**19** The latest figures of graduates trained per year (scientists and engineers combined) are roughly U.K. 13,000, U.S.A. 65,000, U.S.S.R. 130,000.

**20** One-third of Russian graduate engineers are women. It is one of our major follies that, whatever we say, we don't in reality regard women as suitable for scientific careers. We thus neatly divide our pool of potential talent by two.

**21** It might repay investigation to examine precisely what education a hundred alpha plus creative persons in science this century have received. I have a feeling that a surprising proportion have not gone over the strictest orthodox hurdles, such as Part II Physics at Cambridge and the like.

**22** The English temptation is to educate such men in sub-university institutions, which carry an inferior class-label. Nothing could be more ill-judged. One often meets American engineers who, in a narrow professional sense, are less rigorously trained than English products from technical colleges; but the Americans have the confidence, both social and individual, that is helped through having mixed with their equals at universities.

23  I have confined myself to the University population. The kind and number of technicians is another and a very interesting problem.

24  The concentration of our population makes us, of course, more vulnerable also in military terms.

25  There is one curious result in all major industrialised societies. The amount of talent one requires for the primary tasks is greater than any country can comfortably produce, and this will become increasingly obvious. The consequence is that there are no people left, clever, competent and resigned to a humble job, to keep the wheels of social amenities going smoothly round. Postal services, railway services, are likely slowly to deteriorate just because the people who once ran them are now being educated for different things. This is already clear in the United States, and is becoming clear in England.

26  In the United States the Lecture was published in hard covers (Cambridge University Press, 1959).

27  *Encounter*, May 1959, and subsequent issues.

28  J. Bronowski, *The Educated Man in 1984*. (Closing address to the Education Section of the British Association, 1955.)

29  Merle Kling, *New Republic*, 8 April 1957.

30  *New Statesman*, 6 October 1956.

31  *Sunday Times*, 10 and 17 March 1957.

32  I am referring to F. R. Leavis's *Two Cultures? The Significance of C. P. Snow* (first published, *Spectator*, 9 March 1962; republished in hard covers by Chatto and Windus in October 1962).

33  Leavis, *op. cit.*

34  *Spectator*, 23 March 1962 and later issues: other examples occur in the subsequent literature.

35  *Mit der Dummheit kämpfen Götter selbst vergebens.*

**36** S. T. Coleridge, *On the Constitution of Church and State*, chapter v.

**37** It is an interesting reflex of the British situation that the Royal Society, early this century, deliberately excluded from its scope the social sciences and other fields of learning which, in other countries, would be regarded as part of 'science' in its universal sense.

**38** Cf. *The Search* (1934).

**39** Good judges of the academic world, both American and English, sometimes tell me that I over-estimate American higher education.

**40** Cf. Kenneth Richmond's *Culture and General Knowledge* (Methuen, 1963).

**41** Alfred Kazin, *Contemporaries*, pp. 171–8 (Secker & Warburg, 1963).

**42** That is, of course, judged by the standards of all human beings born up to the present time.

**43** Cf. publications of I.N.E.D. (Institut National d'Etudes Démographiques), Paris. See, for example, M. Fleury and L. Henry, *Des registres paroissiaux à l'histoire de la population* (I.N.E.D., 1956); J. Meuvret, *Les crises de subsistances et la démographique de la France d'Ancien Régime. Population* (1946).

**44** I.e. the peasants starved, and a small richer stratum survived. Recent research on seventeenth-century Sweden has shown that a year of semi-starvation was often followed by a year of epidemics which finished off the young, the old, and the debilitated.

**45** E.g. P. Laslett and J. Harrison, '*Clayworth and Cogenhoe*', in *Historical Essays 1600–1750* (A. & C. Black, 1963).

**46** D. H. Lawrence, *Studies in Classic American Literature*, chapter 9.

**47** The pseudo-scientific jargon keeps cropping up through the entire passage.

**48** *The Rainbow*, chapter 12, provides one example out of many. 'Hatred sprang up in Ursula's heart. If she could she would smash the machine. Her soul's action should be the smashing of the great machine. If she could destroy the colliery, and make all the men of Wiggiston out of work, she would do it. Let them starve and grub in the earth for roots, rather than serve such a Moloch as this.'

This is an explicit statement of Luddite convictions: note the use of 'them'. It is *those others* who are exhorted to undergo the sacrifice and pay the price. But if Dostoevsky had been recommending Luddite activites, he wouldn't have stopped at random exhortation: he would have written out a programme by which the machines could be wrecked.

**49** W. H. Auden (incidentally one of the few poets for a hundred years with both a scientific education and scientific insight) put it better in *In Memory of Yeats*.

**50** In both the English and the American senses of the word.

**51** There was an outburst of modernist literature (and other art) in Russia from the death of Chekhov (1904) until the Revolution and slightly after. When contemporary Russians say, as they sometimes do, that they have been through all that and don't think much of it, they are not inventing their case.

**52** Dame Edith Sitwell, on being asked whether she was to be included among modernists or not, replied that whichever way was chosen she would consider it wrong.

**53** *Partisan Review Anthology, 1962.* I might mention that I was perplexed by Trilling's essay about *The Two*

*Cultures* (*Commentary*, June 1959). Nothing is more tedious than a writer claiming he is being misrepresented. It is usually his own fault. But I felt like saying that Trilling was attributing to me views on literature which I haven't expressed and don't hold: and attacking them by expressing views which, in the light of what he has written before and since, he doesn't appear to hold either. Martin Green has taken up the argument, more adequately, eloquently and dispassionately than I could have done: see *Essays in Criticism*, Winter 1963.

**54** Stephen Spender, *The Struggle of the Modern* (Hamish Hamilton, 1962).

**55** Georg Lukács, *The Meaning of Contemporary Realism* (Merlin Press, 1962—originally published in German in 1957).

**56** Harry Levin, *The Gates of Horn* (Oxford, 1963)

**57** I examined this problem in *Science and Government* and in the Appendix (published together, New American Library, 1962).